Beating Cancer Through Faith and Inspiration Using Narratives, Short Stories, Poetry, and Devotionals

Including a Journal for your Medical, Physical, and Emotional Journey

David A. Schwarz III, BFA, BA PSYCH

God has blessed us with another day—don't waste it!

DORRANCE
PUBLISHING CO
EST. 1920
PITTSBURGH, PENNSYLVANIA 15238

Dorrance Publishing Co
585 Alpha Drive
Suite 103
Pittsburgh, PA 15238
Visit our website at *www.dorrancebookstore.com*

ISBN: 978-1-6853-7412-9
eISBN: 978-1-6853-7556-0

I want to recognize my wife Jane Schwarz.. My parents David and Cynthia Schwarz.. My children Landon and Shely Schwarz.. Tim and Alexis Fluitt and Zachary Schwarz for thier love and support in the writing of this book.. A Thank you to my friend and colleague Ron Barden who believed in me and helped me through a very dark time in my life.. My best friend Tony Rex (RIP brother).. And a very special thank you to God and Jesus Christ that has loved me and gifted me to write to help others going through this very challenging time..

Thank you
David A. Schwarz III BFA, BA PSYCH

My Story

I am a cancer Fighter and Survivor and this is my story. I am a proud cancer fighter and survivor and a deeply religious man. I have two Baccalaureate degrees, my second degree in psychology while fighting cancer. I've lived in a half-million-dollar home and I've lived in my car. I've had thousands in the bank and I've had nothing in the bank. I've had $20,000 in my hands and I've had to dig under my car seat to find a quarterr to buy a bean and cheese taco because I was starving. l have had many family and friends in my life and I have been completely alone with no one. All of the extreme circumstances in my life have been due to my bipolar diagnosis, bipolar 1, mixed episode and trying to control this heartbreaking and deadly mental illness. Through many trials with various drugs that were unsuccessful, I finally found a medication that works and normalizes me. As I began to rebuild my life with this medication, I became reacquainted with family and friends and began to rebuild relationships as well as meeting a wonderful woman who would become my wife. I landed a good job and began leading a normal and fulfilling life. Then life threw me another curveball... CANCER.

It began when I had what I thought was a canker sore on the right side of my tongue and for months I ignored the pain. I look back now at how crazy I was not to see a doctor immediately; instead, I decided to deal with the pain. It progressed to the point that I could no longer eat comfortably so I finally made the decision to go to the emergency room at a hospital near me. After hours of waiting, I finally saw a doctor who asked the reason for my visit. I told her that I had a canker sore on my tongue. She took one look and backed away at which time I could see a look of concern on her face. She said, "I have no idea what that is on your tongue." At that point I knew I was in trouble.

She contacted an ENT and set an appointment for the next day. The day was spent doing CT scans, MRI scans and biopsies. Five days later the results were in stage 4 squamous cell carcinoma of the tongue. While the doctor was talking, all I could think of was that my life as I knew it would never be the same, although I had no idea just how much this diagnosis would change my life. I would have to learn to eat solid foods again, learn to talk again, and learn to drink again, to even teach myself to literally breathe again.

One week later I lay in post-op after a 15-hour surgery, three-fourths of my tongue gone, replaced with a flap taken from the thigh muscle of my left leg, 45 lymph nodes removed, of which three were cancerous. I was on a ventilator because of breathing problems. My daughter Lexi was crying because she was afraid to see me in this condition. My mom, my dad and my wife all were looking at me through tears of concern and fear. I was then put into ICU because I needed 24/7 care. I'd never felt so alone and afraid. The pain and the mental anguish at times was overwhelming. I would have lucid moments through my drug-hazed mind.

Cancer affects us in so many other ways than the disease itself, which brings me to the beginning of treatments... radiation.

My next experience with pain was the extracting of all of my bottom teeth and most of my top teeth in preparation for the radiation. This was to prevent the radiation from causing osteoradionecrosis (ORN). However, the plan did not work because I also now have ORN. After they burned me down to my last molecule with 35 rounds of radiation, I went to a very dark place in my life. I lost over 100 pounds and could not eat solid food for over a year. I received all of my nutrition through a peg tube that went straight into my stomach and I would feed protein drinks through it to stay alive. For months I experienced excruciating pain in my mouth from the surgeries and radiation. I had more doctor's appointments, therapy sessions, x-rays, CT scans and MRIs than I can count. Cancer affected me in so many different ways: physically, mentally and emotionally. Cancer, by its very nature, is a physical disease, but it also affects our psyche and our human element both mentally and emotionally.

I am in pain every day of my life. I take medications to deal with the mental and physical torment of this disease. For years I have fought to have a normal life. I finally understand that it will never be normal. Then one day I thought...why can't I combine my love of writing with the pain and frustration of this disease? Writing became therapeutic and altruistic at the same time. I began to write a daily blog/post for a cancer group about three years ago and my writing caught on because others could see I felt the way they did. I could understand their pain and what they had to traverse in their daily lives. I was able, with God's blessing, to help others through my writing. I then was invited to write in another, then another. I now write in fifteen different Cancer Support Groups. I have my posts up by 5 A.M. every morning in all fifteen groups. I am so happy and so blessed to be able to impact the lives of others with my writings.

I would not wish this disease on my worst enemy, but at the same time I am thankful that God has directed me to use my writing to help other warriors fighting this horrible disease. I decided to put my pain to use by writing positive devotionals on how to cope mentally through optimism, strength and courage.

I hope you find these devotionals helpful so that you can live a life dictated by you and not cancer. A life of strength, courage and resiliency... a life you want to wake up to... a life worth living.

> *He renews my strength... He guides me along right paths*
> *bringing honor to His name.*
> *Psalm 23:3*

Likes, Loves and Comments about My Narratives

Peggy Waldron (Survivors of Tongue Cancer)
Your words are so helpful to so many. You have given me much inspiration and guidance!

Debbie Dicker Ruchetti (Survivors of Tongue Cancer)
You have helped so many with your morning posts. You are one of the great people who has come into my life.

Kathleen Oreste (Survivors of Tongue Cancer)
Thank you so much for sharing your gift of writing with us... Your posts always move me... and make me want to fight for life.

Jackie Campbell (Cancer Support Group for Patients and Their Families)
I truly look forward to your posts. They are inspirational and quite frankly a slap in the face. You make us want to push through to another day. Thank you for your words.

Cynthia Breslin (Cancer Support Group)
Thank you for this!! I was diagnosed terminal and that doesn't give me hope... but reading this I now have hope again.

Donna Carson Gerdes (Cancer Support Group)
Thank you for your words. You show me that there is purpose for my life. I'm not quitting thanks to you.

Bev Aalbers (Cancer Support Group)

Thank you! I'm grateful to start every day with your inspirational words. They make a huge difference in my life...changing me into a more positive person.

Alice Harkness (Cancer Support Group for Patients and Their Families)

Please don't ever stop our messages. I am saving every one of them, and when I am having a bad day I go back and read them. You are an inspiration to me and others. God Bless you.

Josie O'Shea (Head and Neck/Oral Cancer Chat and Support)

Love your posts. They have helped me get through the last twelve months. Thank you so much for your words.

Julie Warrick (Head and Neck/Oral Cancer Chat and Support)

Oh my Goodness!! This!! This right here!! What you wrote says it all!! Wow!! Amazing!! Thank you!!

Judie Smith (Head and Neck/Oral Cancer Chat and Support)

I look forward to reading your posts every morning! They are the highlight of my day! Your optimism and positive attitude make me strive to be a better person!

Amy Springer (Head and Neck/Oral Cancer Chat and Support)

Thank you. I am at the beginning of my journey but your words are already helping me!

Jill Quiggy Spencer (Head and Neck/Oral Cancer Chat and Support)

Each day I love, enjoy and appreciate your moving and real posts. You are great at expression!

Rebecca Corbitt (Head and Neck/Oral Cancer Chat and Support)

Thank you again. You amaze me. I just feel broken, then I read your messages and regain my strength.

Dana Kumerow (Survivors of Tongue Cancer)
Thank you... really needed this...Your words put me back on track and show me the way.

Chris Purvis (Survivors of Head and Neck Cancer)
Reading your posts make me happy to be alive.

Stormie Bruegger (Head and Neck/Oral Cancer Chat and Support)
I want to let you know that I read your posts regularly since I joined the group... and your posts are what gave me courage to share my story...Thank you so much.

Clarice King (Head and Neck/Oral Cancer Chat and Support)
Love this and it can be a message to all who are going through any type of difficulty: divorce, addiction, etc. Would love to see you do an inspirational page for the public. Your words are always uplifting and everyone can benefit from your inspirational words.

The names of the groups that many warriors belong to are in parentheses. Please join one or all of these groups because it can be life changing to talk to and interact with all of these individuals and you can be part of the team. Part of something bigger...part of a family that understands how you feel every day and that has the ability to see you through the trials and tribulations of what this disease can do to you not only physically but mentally and emotionally as well. Become part of the bigger picture...being able to talk and interact with others going through exactly what you're going through makes this journey so much easier and you will know that you are not alone...you are part of a group or groups that have the ability to guide you through a very tough and intensely personal journey.

User Guide

This book/journal covers 90 days of your personal journey.

This book/journal allows the reader to accept their intensely personal journey along with the utility use of a journal to chronicle their journey...

This book/journal includes a daily narrative and devotional meant to be used one day at a time. Each day starts with an inspirational narrative followed by a devotional from the Bible on the first page. The second page consists of three positive comments from previous readers on how the day's narrative and devotional affects their lives and the influence on their days so that the reader can see and acknowledge that they are part of a bigger picture and how the narrative/ devotional affects them. This is followed by a prompt journal where the reader can journal every day on how they feel and what they can accomplish that day. Schedule doctor appointments, treatments, surgeries, etc., as well as plan out their agenda/activity for that day and then write down final thoughts at bedtime. These narratives/devotionals will help the reader deal with their concerns one day at a time in a positive way mentally, physically, and emotionally as well as spiritually to deal with whatever cancer can burden them with that day and every day thereafter.

Date _____

Example page 1.

Forget

When did we forget to laugh...
When did we forget to smile...
When did we forget to dance...
When did we forget to have fun for a while...
When did we forget our passion...
When did we forget our joy...
When did we forget to once again play with our toys...

My friends... this disease steals our food... it steals our sleep... it steals our strength... but most of all it steals our time... it consumes us as we wake up... as we sleep and every second in between... this disease can overwhelm our days and nights... it will never let us forget... it will try to sever our relationship with family and friends... our relationship with God... our relationship with you...

If you are reading this... God has gifted you another day, don't waste it... use today as another day to inspire... another day to teach... another day to hit the reset button... another day to find the pieces to the puzzle... another chance to find what we have lost... we did not fight through surgeries... radiation therapies... chemo sessions and pain every day to sit in the dark and feel sorry for ourselves... we fought through the beast to live... to have a chance to laugh... to smile... to dance... to have fun for a while... we fight to keep our passion... we fight to keep our joy... we fight to find our happiness because we have a life to enjoy...

He will once again fill your mouth with laughter and your lips with shouts of joy. Job 8:21

Date _____

Example page 2

Forget – Comments

Carla Van Vranken (Survivors of Tongue Cancer)
That was beautiful. So grateful. Thank you for the encouragement!

Cliff How (Head and Neck/Oral Cancer Chat and Support)
Could not have said it better myself. Thank you for helping me fight!

Toni Cignciarulo Hoover (Cancer Survivors)
Inspiring. The best!

Morning Thoughts:

Day's Agenda/Activities/Medications:

Dr. Appointments/Treatments/Therapies:

Bedtime Thoughts:

Date _____

Mental

Good Morning, Fighters

Dealing with the psychological effects of cancer are just as important if not more important than dealing with the physical effects alone... our mental health is overlooked way too often ... the unmitigated impact of depression... anxiety... PTSD... survivor's guilt and other mental illnesses change who we are inside and out... dealing with a new self-image... looking in the mirror and seeing only the negative challenges cancer has caused... we have many visible scars but we have many invisible scars as well... the internal struggles we all go through... this topic is not talked about nearly enough... if you are experiencing any of these issues speak up and get the help you need... we are just as fragile mentally as we are physically when fighting cancer... you are not weak if you ask for help... others will not look down on you or view you differently... (if they do you don't need them in your life anyway)... go see a trained professional ... a psychologist...a psychiatrist or therapist... doing so may not just help you heal but save your life as well... this unbelievably important topic needs to be talked about... talked about so loudly that everyone can hear... our mental health is vital to beating cancer and healing mind... body and soul...

Even when I walk through the darkest valley
I will not be afraid, for you are close beside me,
your rod and your staff protect and comfort me.
Psalm 23:4

Date _____

Mental – Comments

Roohi Naeen (Cancer Survivors and Supporters)
You are so right. Every word is important.

Kate Brice (Cancer Support Group)
I could not have said it any better. "Thank you."

TB Pats (Head and Neck/Oral Cancer Chat and Support)
You are our ray of sunshine and our major motivator. Thank you.

Morning Thoughts:

Day's Agenda/Activities/Medications:

Dr. Appointments/Treatments/Therapies:

Bedtime Thoughts:

Date _____
Jigsaw Puzzle
Good Morning, Fighters

As cancer fighters we are a jigsaw puzzle of struggle... frustration ... pain and fear... we are scared of the unknown and unidentified... petrified of something we cannot see... a thought that we will break... mind... body and soul... we feel under attack... physically... mentally and emotionally...what we once considered fair is now an anomaly...we are afraid for tomorrow... we want today to be over before it begins... the full weight of the unknown on our shoulders as the word cancer bulldozes our every thought not giving us a moment's peace... we fight to understand this unseen enemy as it tears at the fabric of our lives... this enemy who pervades our very essence while trying to destroy us and shake our foundation... trying to make us mistrust...disrupt and change our reality... or what we thought reality was...

We scream in our minds, "Why me, God," over and over... every day bleeds into the next as we bleed from our wounds... the visible scars that define us to strangers and the invisible scars that define us to those we love... as we search for our peace in the pieces...we must realize that our new reality is a jigsaw puzzle... and like any great puzzle it takes time to put the pieces back into place... you can't force the wrong piece into the wrong hole or the whole puzzle crashes... it takes an abundance of strength... courage and patience to put the puzzle back together... each day a new piece falls into place... the puzzle slowly comes into focus and begins to reveal a stronger more courageous and better you... so have patience and perseverance and one day you will be able to look in the mirror at the finished puzzle and tell yourself with a smile...

"You are an amazing human being." God
"My grace is all you need...my power works best in weakness."

So now I am glad to boast about my weaknesses...so that the power of Christ can work through me.
2 Corinthians 12:9

Date _____
Jigsaw Puzzle – Comments

Gloria B. Thomas (Head and Neck/Oral Cancer Chat and Support)
You are a daily inspiration and help us fight the good fight.

Cee Gerda (Head and Neck/Oral Cancer Chat and Support)
Amen. Thank you for this.

Randall Alderman (Cancer Survivors Network)
Amazing!

Morning Thoughts:

Day's Agenda/Activities/Medications:

Dr. Appointments/Treatments/Therapies:

Bedtime Thoughts:

Date _____

15 Rounds

Good Morning, Fighters

A cancer diagnosis is the opening bell to a 15-round title fight. We are in the ring vs. a tough and resilient competitor... an opponent that doesn't fight fair... that will sucker punch us... that abides by no rules... that will kick us when we're down... that wants us to give up... it's us vs. cancer, my friends... cancer takes the first 10 rounds by default (biopsies... surgeries... chemo... radiation)... cancer is beating the hell out of us and our hands are tied... for 10 rounds we are bloody and beaten... barely able to stand... wanting to say no more... wanting to give up... then comes round 11 (treatment is over)... it's time to start healing... we begin to punch back... we are now trading blows with this unrelenting opponent... as the fight continues we get stronger and stronger... we can feel the life flowing back into our veins... we are beginning to beat cancer down... now is when we flip the switch... give it all we have and win this fight by a knockout...

We do this by...
pushing ourselves to eat...rest and exercise...
listening to and following our doctor's plans for us...
taking our medications the correct way...
doing the right thing...
making tough choices...
having belief and faith in God and ourselves...

In round 15 we take back our life... we take back who we are... we take back control...we take back our soul... we may be a little beaten up... we may be a little sore... we may have some bruises and are a little bloody but we are still standing... still fighting... as the final bell rings we can proudly hold our fists in the air and scream at the top of our lungs, "I am a fighter... I am a survivor... I am a winner."

*Having hope will give you courage. You will be
protected and will rest in safety.
Job 11:18*

Date _____

15 Rounds – Comments

Crissy Garcia Florio (Cancer Support Group)
This is amazing!!! Thank you for sharing.

Alice Harkness (Cancer Support Group)
Thank you. This is just what I needed right now. You have given me the inspiration to fight.

Deborah Calloway (Head and Neck/Oral Cancer Chat and Support)
Your words are like a morning sermon to me. Thank you.

Morning Thoughts:

Day's Agenda/Activities/Medications:

Dr. Appointments/Treatments/Therapies:

Bedtime Thoughts:

Date _____
Choice

Good Morning, Fighters

Cancer was not our choice... but our attitude on how we approach it is our choice... the choices are difficult... there is nothing easy about cancer... we must choose through tears... we must choose through fears... we must choose through blinding rage... every choice we make while fighting this disease is life changing...we must believe in ourselves and our choices... our choices dictate our attitude and our attitude dictates the life we are fighting for... crying for... praying for...it's amazing what we can do if we believe in ourselves and our choices...

To those of you who have just been diagnosed... to those of you who are waiting on scan and biopsy results... to those of you who have just begun treatment or are in the middle of your fight... to those who are beginning to heal are starting to feel like yourselves again... I give you great news... I give you something to look forward to... I share with you the lives of the many who have beaten this disease... we are running miles... lifting weights... riding bikes... climbing mountains... singing... traveling the world... we are very active in our new lives... some of us are even stronger now than before... we've stared down this beast and won just like every one of you will do...

We've accomplished this by getting out of bed when we didn't want to... by eating right... exercising... taking our meds as prescribed... listening to our doctors and nurses... making those tough choices... my friends, there is life after cancer... and it can be one hell of a great life... all it takes is belief in ourselves and our choices... to have that belief will make your attitude one of positivity...optimism... hope and courage... you are a true life warrior...no matter what stage you are in you've got this... a little belief in ourselves and our choices is what will win this fight... will win this war...

So let us come boldly to the throne of our gracious God. There we will
receive his mercy and we will find grace to help us when we need it most...
Hebrews 4:16

Date _____
Choice – Comments

Ann Hall (Cancer Support Group for Patients)
Thank you for your encouraging words...

Jacki Campbell (Cancer Support Group for Patients)
Much needed today.

Michael Stevenson (Cancer Support Group)
Thank you, for your words. You are truly an inspiration my friend.

Morning Thoughts:

Day's Agenda/Activities/Medications:

Dr. Appointments/Treatments/Therapies:

Bedtime Thoughts:

Date _____

The Poem

Good Morning, Fighters

I was going through some paperwork and ran across this poem that I wrote while in the midst of surgeries and treatment... a very painful and dark time.

  If touched do I not feel...
if wounded will I not heal... in pain will I not cry...
to God will I ask why
if pushed will I react
in truth will I find fact...
at dawn will I not rise...
in time will I be wise
if loved do I love back...
in strength will I not lack...
if tired will I not sigh
in time will I not die...
cancer is in my head...

at times I would rather be dead... but through this I will fight...
from morning until the dead of night...
cancer, you will not win...
for my health I will begin...
to beat this ugly disease...
this is the day I will seize...
my new life I will embrace...
with positivity...courage and grace...

My friends, we can take solace in knowing we are not alone in this fight... we are all in this together... we all have each other's backs... we are a very powerful gang... so carpe diem (seize the day), my friends... this is the only day that we will have exactly like this one in our lives... so let's find our passion... what drives you... what can take your mind off of fighting for just a little while...

writing... painting... fixing up old cars... building... or simply a walk in the park... find something that makes you smile... makes you happy ... makes you want to get out of bed... makes you want to get your mind right... do something constructive... if you can do this you will watch the pain and anger slip away...

Your words are a lamp for my feet.
A light on my path.
Psalm 119:105

Date _____
The Poem – Comments

Marilyn Ruedisveli (Head and Neck/Oral Cancer Chat and Support)
Such soul searching and touching words. Thank you for touching our hearts.

Gloria b. Thomas (Head and Neck/Oral Cancer Chat and Support)
Your writings are my morning inspiration.

Donna Baker (Survivors of Tongue Cancer)
You bring my passion to live and enjoy what the day brings me.

Morning Thoughts:

Day's Agenda/Activities/Medications:

Dr. Appointments/Treatments/Therapies:

Bedtime Thoughts:

Date _____
The Past

Good Morning, Fighters

I had someone tell me yesterday... "Keep moving forward... don't look back"... I'm sure you guys have heard this statement or a variation of it many times... this time I began to think... to keep moving forward... I absolutely agree... but to never look back, I completely disagree... in my humble opinion to look back at our lives is not a sin... to draw strength from our past successes no matter how small is a key to healing... to remember our good days... our positive circumstances and situations... to think back with a smile... to learn from our mistakes so that we don't repeat them... to remember what has worked for us and what has not... to use our painful moments and memories as motivation to move forward... to look back at who was there for us and who disappeared... to never forget who we are and how hard we fought to get to our present situation... we can use the past to change our perspective ... to change our thought process... to change our attitude... by using our knowledge of the past we can change our circumstances and those around us into a positive light... we can even change ourselves, which in turn will change our aura... our energy... our kinesis so that our infectious positivity permeates those around us... so that others raise an eyebrow and smile because we smile... to use yesterday to break through the challenges of today... so others can see our will to win... that our will to win is inspirational... to change those around us with our attitude... we can use our past in so many wonderful ways... to lead a life of positivity, not obscurity... to make today a day to remember and not forget... a day of not living in the past but using it for a better future...

> *We who have fled from the refuge of the future*
> *must have strong encouragement to hold fast*
> *to the hope set before us today.*
> *Hebrews 6:18*

Date _____

The Past – Comments

Mary Ann Schofield (Survivors of Tongue Cancer)
You're always moving us forward with words of wisdom.

Guinn Nexen (Survivors of Head and Neck Cancer)
Amen... amen... amen... continue to use your words of love and encourage others.

Terri Knudsen (Head and Neck/Oral Cancer Chat and Support)
The past makes us who we are today. Great words.

Morning Thoughts:

Day's Agenda/Activities/Medications:

Dr. Appointments/Treatments/Therapies:

Bedtime Thoughts:

Date _____

2 Ways

Good Morning, Fighters

Cancer changes how we look at life... how we look at death and every second in between... it changes how we look... how we taste... how we smell... it changes our business life... our sex life... our personal life... it changes our relationships with family and friends... it changes how we walk... how we talk... how we eat and in some cases how we breathe... it changes our relationship with God and Jesus... it changes our relationship with ourselves... cancer can make us weaker or stronger...it can make us angry and frustrated or it can make us more understanding and forgiving... it can hide who we are or bring out our best selves...

We have many reasons to give up... many reasons to lie in bed all day... many reasons to be resentful and pissed off at the world... many reasons to become distant and push others away... or we can find many reasons to become closer to friends and loved ones than we have ever been before...

When it comes down to how we live this life we have 2 choices;

We can let this disease beat us down... let it steal our joy... let it fundamentally change who we are... to live a lonely and painful existence... to be alive but not to live.

or

We can fight this disease with every fiber of who we are... we can beat it down... to live a positive and inclusive existence... to go to a place where cancer does not rule us but we rule it... to not only be alive but to live...

"Which choice will you make today, my friends?"

He will cover you with his feathers. He will shelter with you with his wings.
His faithful promises are your armor and protection.
Psalm 91:4

Date _____

2 Ways – Comments

Elisa Maria Argiro (Cancer Support Group)
So profoundly true. Thank you for this.

Linda Marie Abramski Rose (Cancer Support for Patients and Their Families)
Beautifully expressed. God bless you.

Jeff Brock (Head and Neck/Oral Cancer Chat and Support)
Perfect speech. You should be a preacher.

Morning Thoughts:

Day's Agenda/Activities/Medications:

Dr. Appointments/Treatments/Therapies:

Bedtime Thoughts:

Date _____
Communication
Good Morning, Fighters

We must deal with the difficulty to tell friends and family hello... we try to grasp the meaning as our minds are filled with thoughts that were never there before... we try to express how we feel but it's hard to put our turmoil into words... others couldn't possibly understand the difference within us that cancer brings... they can only see the outside which is a facsimile of who we are on the inside... the mental strain of this disease is twice that of anything it can do to us physically... our rage at the pain can't be imagined... this disease will push us to the very edge and will test our guts as it tries to expose every weakness... communication is the key to healing inside and out... to interact with others who can understand our pain and what we face every day...someone who can understand our victories as well as guide us through our defeats... to be able to interact with another warrior who can't eat solid food... who must eat through a tube or has to breathe through a trach... to communicate with a warrior who can provide technical and moral support... someone who provides a shoulder to lean on when we are having a bad day... warriors that can understand the pure unadulterated anger that we have at this disease... we must communicate with our brothers and sisters in the fight... to share our experiences is priceless... to know we are not alone... that we fight together... that we share a will to survive... a will to face this enemy together... a will to scream at this disease... "You will not beat me"... to know you have back up... to know we fought our butts off yesterday to live today... I want to say thank you to each of you... just knowing you are there has saved me many a sleepless night and has allowed me to remember who I was before all of this... we can and will make it through together... we can and will approach each day with fire in our veins... strength in our resolve... winning on our minds and faith in our souls... to have humility... ..love and respect for each other... my brothers and sisters... you guys are my extended family and I could not be more proud... much love and respect...

I want to encourage you in your faith. But I also want to be encouraged by yours. Romans 1:12

Date _____
Communication – Comments

John Heath (Survivors of Tongue Cancer)
Great words from a super guy!! Thank you.

Donna Parker (Survivors of Tongue Cancer)
I read your words every day. Your words are my encouragement to keep fighting and battle every day.

Pam Baranski Thompson (Head and Neck/Oral Cancer Chat and Support)
You are my main inspiration.

Morning Thoughts:

Day's Agenda/Activities/Medications:

Dr. Appointments/Treatments/Therapies:

Bedtime Thoughts:

Date _____

Faith

Good Morning, Fighters

Faith... what a beautiful word... keep the faith... I have faith in you... have faith in me... I have faith in God and Jesus... words of faith... there are many ways and different contexts of the word faith and how it is used... what a power-ful...strong... all-encompassing word... a word that transcends the physical world... the human mentality... when we were born into this world... faith was already within us...

If we have faith in this world... faith in God almighty... faith in Jesus Christ... faith in other people... faith in strength and courage... faith in ourselves... then this fight means something ... with faith there is purpose... faith makes life worth living... faith makes this fight worth fighting...

When we fall we have faith we can rise again... when we want to run faith keeps us firm... faith is bigger than our anxieties and fears... faith gives us mo-tivation and purpose... it gives us something to live for... something to fight for... faith gets us out of bed... gets us dressed... gives us a reason to meet today... faith gives us optimism and hope... the word faith has won wars... it's seen many a warrior through the battlefield ... faith is a beautiful combination of hope and spirit... faith allows us to face our darkest fears... faith gives us im-mense strength and inspiration to fight... to beat this disease... to stand together as one to beat cancer... to have faith in ourselves and what we've en-dured...thru faith we will watch the sun rise... we will open our eyes to a beautiful world... through faith we laugh together... we cry together... we fight together... through faith we will never give up or give in... having unmitiga-ting... unconditional... unwavering faith is how we win... without faith there are no miracles... with faith there is a miracle around every corner... faith... what a beautiful word...

*You have been set apart as holy to the Lord your God
and he has chosen you from all the nations on earth
to be his own special treasure. Thank you for forgiving
me and loving me unconditionally.*
Deuteronomy 14:12

Date _____
Faith – Comments

Peg Lewis Wilcott (Head and Neck/Oral Cancer Chat and Support)
What beautiful words and so... so true.

Julie Warrick (Head and Neck/Oral Cancer Chat and Support)
This is my favorite so far. I needed this today. Thank you.

Melissa Ann (Head and Neck/Oral Cancer Chat and Support)
I love your daily words of encouragement.

Morning Thoughts:

Day's Agenda/Activities/Medications:

Dr. Appointments/Treatments/Therapies:

Bedtime Thoughts:

Date _____

Future

Good Morning, Fighters

As I lie awake I can feel the life within me... I feel the rhythmic beat of my heart... I feel the fight within my soul... today I look to the future...

What does the word 'future' really mean... ..is it a set of predetermined circumstances... is it random... do we have control over our future... has God decided our future for us... what about those we love do we determine their future or do they determine ours... what about those we pretend to ignore... what is their role... the car driving next to us... the bus driver... the pilot... people we will never see again... what role do random circumstances play... I had Machiavellian thinking about the future... I took the future for granted... the future was a given... the future is as solid as a whisp of smoke...

Post diagnosis the term future has taken on new meaning. It now has a basis... the future now has a concrete meaning of hope and healing... it signals a better tomorrow... looking to the future helps us deal with today's pain... anxiety and depression ... we covet the future... the future gives us tomorrow... it is why we get out of bed... why we wait patiently for biopsy and scan results... why we undergo 15-hour surgeries that leave both physical and mental scars... why we accept the burning radiation and the poison being forced into our veins... the blood on our pillow... the excruciating pain...

The future is our motivation... the future is why we smile... the future is why we have faith and courage... the future is what gives us hope for tomorrow... for next week... next month... for next year... the future is how we get through... it gives us the opportunity to make this world a better place... to make today a day to remember and not forget... the future is why we exist... if you're reading this God has blessed you another day... don't waste it... use today's gift to look to the future... the future is how we heal... the future is for real...

You must love the Lord your God with all your heart; all your soul; all your strength.
   Deuteronomy 6:5

Date _____
Future – Comments

Melissa n Ken Haff (Survivors of Tongue Cancer)
I am sitting here crying reading this.

CA Andrews (Survivors of Head and Neck Cancer)
*Another day I got out of bed to read your inspirational thought and thank God
for your talent.*

Frankie Clark (Survivors of Head and Neck Cancer)
I just love your quotes and power of thinking.

Morning Thoughts:

Day's Agenda/Activities/Medications:

Dr. Appointments/Treatments/Therapies:

Bedtime Thoughts:

Date _____

2 Choices

Good Morning, Fighters

Does cancer change our lives... absolutely it does... does cancer put barriers in our path... absolutely it does... cancer try to turn us into someone we are not? Absolutely it does... let's get down to brass tacks this morning... let's be completely honest with ourselves...we can only fool ourselves and others for so long...when it comes down to where the rubber meets the road we have 2 choices:

We can lie in bed all day feeling sorry for ourselves...angry and pissed off at the world... giving up on life and our future. wasting away our potential and then ultimately wasting away ...

<<or>>

We can get up and get out there and live... is it going to be easy... hell no, it's not... life doesn't change to fit you... life doesn't work for you... life doesn't say, "Oh, I'm sorry, David, here, let me help you"... life is for people that want to grab their piece of the pie... people that don't use lame excuses or has a 'why me' attitude... life makes us work for it... work to be successful... work to beat this disease... work for the feeling of accomplishment... this pertains to everyone in life... even more so for us as fighters of cancer... we not only fight cancer but we fight the same everyday issues as everyone else... we must fight twice as hard for the same results... is any of this fair... nope... we are all going to have 'why me' moments... we are human... just don't let those moments turn into hours or days... don't let them consume you... my friends, there is a great big world out there waiting for your DNA... a world that will test your strength and resilience... your courage and hope... a life that will test who you are as a person.. we must endure and fight for our health and for a piece of the pie as well... no matter how big or small it's your piece.. and one thing I am absolutely sure of is life rewards a fighter... much respect for each and every one of you... believe me when I tell you... we are some of the strongest people on earth...

You have allowed me to suffer much hardship but you will restore me to life again and give me choices and lift me from the depths of the earth. Help me to see life through your eyes and to deepen my relationship with you.
Psalm 71:20

Date _____

2 Choices – Comments

Erin Jayne Colson (Cancer Support Group for Patients and Their Families)
Love it. Extremely well said.

Christine Brower (Survivors of Head and Neck Cancer)
I so enjoy reading your posts.

Jennifer Kolezynski (Cancer Support Group)
Thank you for this. It is exactly what I needed today.

Morning Thoughts:

Day's Agenda/Activities/Medications:

Dr. Appointments/Treatments/Therapies:

Bedtime Thoughts:

Date _____

Adapt

Good Morning, Fighters

Adaption is a strength not to be underestimated... it has been part of the human condition since the beginning of time... it is one of God's graces... adaption is part of the human spirit... we are constantly adapting... we must adapt to how we approach life every day... when it's raining we adapt... when it's cold we adapt... when we have children we adapt... when we marry we adapt... when we drive we adapt... at work we adapt... when someone dies we adapt... every day we adapt to new circumstances ... God has blessed us with the ability to adapt to anything in life...

For us being able to adapt is essential...we must adapt to a new way of life... a new way to live... adaption is key to beating this disease... we must be strategic as to how we adapt to our new lives... there is nothing we can't overcome by thinking it through... adjusting and adapting to the challenges before us...

7 rules to adapting to our new life:

Have patience... patience is a must when adapting to a new life.

Stay calm... we make better decisions when we are calm

It's on us... we are in charge of our attitude and decisions which helps us adapt.

Keep fighting... as long as we are fighting we are adapting.

Keep it together... sometimes we get overwhelmed. take a step back and breathe.

Have a sense of humor... smiles and laughter help us heal... help us think... help us make positive decisions...

Have hope...with hope we will be able to handle the challenges in a positive and optimistic way, which will facilitate adaptation to a better life.

Adaptation is the key that opens the door to success...to be able to adapt to our new normal... adaptation is vital to living a life that shines...a life of fulfillment... happiness... positivity and optimism... adaption is life...

> *The Lord will guide you continually giving you water when you are dry*
> *and restore your strength. You will be like a well-watered garden.*
> *Like an overflowing spring.*
> *Isaiah 58:11*

:

Date _____
Adapt – Comments

Linnette Cruz Vallenllanes (Survivors of Tongue Cancer)
Wow what a great message. I love it.

Brenna Baker (Cancer Support Group)
Thank you. I needed those words.

Paul Sands (Head and Neck/Oral Cancer Chat and Support)
Thumbs up. Great read.

Morning Thoughts:

Day's Agenda/Activities/Medications:

Dr. Appointments/Treatments/Therapies:

Bedtime Thoughts:

Date _____
Steps
Good Morning, Fighters

For us getting out of bed takes more guts than the average person getting through the entire day... yes, I said guts because we have to dig deep... we have to fight off the pain both mentally and physically to put our feet on the floor... to then rise... at times it takes every ounce of strength we have to take that first step to begin the day... that first step is the most difficult and the most important because it leads to the second step which becomes a little easier... and with steps 3 and 4 we begin to believe and begin to tell ourselves, "I've got this"... "I'm going to make it"... the next steps we take are with purpose and meaning... we have now become part of the living experience... part of the fabric of life interwoven into the details... no matter how small we now make a difference... we now impact life around us... just knowing that simple truth makes us a much happier person... even if we have a tough day we can say, "I got my butt out of bed," and that, my friends, means something...

The morning moves forward and our life begins to take shape... we begin our version of a normal life... yes, at times we are tired and worn out... upset with the pain... being part of life is key to our recovery both mentally and physically... without even realizing it we validate ourselves and our existence and begin to validate those around us... others gain strength by watching our fight... we have the strength of Hercules... the courage of MLK... the attitude of Ali and the patience of job... we are unicorns... we must approach our new life with the intensity and wonderment of a child... we must adapt to this new life... so let's give today all we have... whether that's running a marathon or just walking the hospital hallways... a 10-mile run or a walk around the block... lifting 5 lbs. or 500 lbs... . doing 1 pushup or 100 of them... it means we are moving forward and telling cancer, 'not today'... 'I will crush you today'... 'I will win this day'... you can count on it..all it takes is that first step!!!

> *For the Lord your God is living among you. He is a*
> *mighty savior. He will take delight in you with gladness*
> *with his love he will calm your fears.*
> *Zephaniah 3:17*

Date _____
Steps – Comments

Patricia Dempsey (Survival of Head and Neck Cancer)
Beautiful. Thank you.

Wanda Wood Buday (Cancer Support Group for Patients and Their Families)
Perfectly said. What you put into words will always be in my head. Thank you.

Kittee Cath (Head and Neck/Oral Cancer Chat and Support)
Wow these are awesome thoughts and words. Inspiration to fight by.

Morning Thoughts:

Day's Agenda/Activities/Medications:

Dr. Appointments/Treatments/Therapies:

Bedtime Thoughts:

Date _____

Good Day, Bad Day

Good Morning, Fighters

We want to make a fist and punch the air as if cancer was standing right in front of us... we want to scream in frustration and turn red with anger as we cuss at a blank wall... we want something tangible to fight...something to focus our anger on... but cancer is a very elusive enemy... we must fight this invisible foe not with our fists but with our strength of character... we must rise above these primal instincts...

Others are watching us... learning from us... praying for us... talking about us... drawing strength from us... waiting for us to show them the way and what today will bring... our friends and family ... our neighbors ... our coworkers and cohorts are all very sensitive to our battles...our challenges... how we handle our adversity...

Every morning we have that all important decision to make... the one decision that impacts everything... it not only impacts our physical health but our mental and emotional health as well... it affects our productivity ... our relationships ... our happiness and our purpose... this decision affects whether we move forward or get left behind...

My friends, the world does not stop turning because we have cancer... it rolls on... life continues... it's up to us to keep up... it's perfectly ok to have a bad day ... we all have them... but begin to lay the groundwork for a good day tomorrow... sometimes it takes every ounce of courage and strength to make this all-important decision... "Will I have a good day or a bad day"... sometimes having a good day can be as elusive as the cancer itself... but a good day is just a decision away... yes, life can be that simple... I think I will choose to have a good day!!

The Lord has heard my plea, the Lord will answer my prayers.
Psalm 6:9

Date _____

Good Day, Bad Day – Comments

Kevin Puckett (Cancer Support Group)
Thank you. Well put!!

Jimmy Cook (Head and Neck/Oral Cancer Chat and Support)
You're right. Thank you—you inspire me to carry on.

Windy Hale (Head and Neck/Oral Cancer Chat and Support)
I am with you!! Today will be a great day!

Morning Thoughts:

Day's Agenda/Activities/Medications:

Dr. Appointments/Treatments/Therapies:

Bedtime Thoughts:

Date _____

Rejoice

Good Morning, Fighters

My friends, it's ok not to be ok... it's ok not to be strong... it's ok to question... it's ok to cry... it's ok to be frustrated... it's ok to be pissed off... we can't define who we are by these negative feelings... my friends, this struggle is real...this fight is tough... we all have these feelings sometimes... we are not weak... we are not different... we are simply human... we are people...

No matter how difficult... painful or disappointing yesterday was... if it was a day of despair... a day of infamy... it was just that... it was yesterday... it is the past... we cannot let yesterday dictate who we are today... what's awesome about today is God gives us the beautiful task of hitting the reset button and begin a brand-new day... a day of redemption... a day to reap the rewards of why we fought so hard yesterday...to give ourselves credit for a job well done... to let cancer know we are not going anywhere... to let cancer know we are going to give it hell today...

The sun is rising so let's get ready to light up the world... to put our imprint on today... to not forget... to marvel at the little things in life... to find passion in the routine and mundane... if we can follow these simple guidelines our lives will become one of wonder not negativity... of love, not hate... to meet today with a positive attitude... to find joy in the details... life can be so great if we just let it... sometimes we get so caught up in the fight we forget that life is right in front of us... all we have to do is reach out and bring it in... and wrap our arms and minds around it...

So today as we open our eyes... let's open our hearts and minds as well and let life in... I promise you won't regret it...

> *Those who know your name have trust in you oh Lord.*
> *Do not abandon those who search for you. Fill them with*
> *love and hope. They believe in your promises. I know*
> *Lord you will never leave me.*
> *Psalm 9:10*

Date _____
Rejoice – Comments

Donna Baker (Survivors of Tongue Cancer)
Thank you for the inspiration to look forward to another day.

Ross Morton (Cancer Support Group)
Great advice. Thank you.

Michael Stevenson (Head and Neck/Oral Cancer Chat and Support)
Your words are helping me to learn this. Your inspiration is great. Thank you.

Morning Thoughts:

Day's Agenda/Activities/Medications:

Dr. Appointments/Treatments/Therapies:

Bedtime Thoughts:

Date _____
My Life

Good Morning, Fighters

As I awoke this morning, I began thinking about my life... I began thinking about the people... places and times that have graced my existence. that I thought impossible a few short years ago... when we get a diagnosis of cancer, our world becomes very small... the future gets dark... the fabric of our soul tears apart... this is when we must make a decision to fight... to believe in our heart and soul that we want to live... to believe it in every fiber of our being...

Cancer had me down for the count... ready to throw in the towel... ready to give up... I didn't think the pain and frustration of the disease was worth it. That day I made the decision of how my life would unfold... I decided to fight with everything I am... I fought through some tough, dark days... there is nothing easy about this disease... God blessed me for my fight as he has every one of you... I began to understand and am now so happy I did because God has given me a multitude of miracles... both my son's wife and my daughter are pregnant. I'm going to be a pops or pawpaw or whatever they want to call me (lol)... my son has landed a great job and he has a wonderful and loving wife... my daughter is married to a good, solid man that takes great care of her. My other son has fought through some challenges but is doing well and is a great kid... I'm married to a wonderful, loving woman who has been by my side through it all... I was blessed with a great mom and dad that have seen me through... these are my blessings...

Your blessings are different than mine, but you have them... just open your eyes and look... they are everywhere... life is worth living... you may not understand it now but you must fight... God favors fighters... the harder you fight the greater the reward... the pain and frustrations are worth it... I chose to fight and live and I am blessed for that fight just as you will be... there are great things ahead... great people and relationships that will come into your life... whatever your situation count your blessings because they are all around you...

*Even when I walk through the darkest valley, I will not
be afraid, for you are close beside me, your rod and
your staff protect and comfort me.*
Psalm 23:4

Date _____

My Life – Comments

Kathy Joann Eddins (Head and Neck/Oral Cancer Chat and Support)
Thank you. I was really struggling today... your words hit home and helped me reevaluate my thoughts.

Ann Louise Hartman (Head and Neck/Oral Cancer Chat and Support)
Thank you for your wonderful words!! I really appreciate you and your words of inspiration.

Nancy Wyatt (Head and Neck/Oral Cancer Chat and Support)
I love your messages. They help me... and I am just a caregiver.

Morning Thoughts:

Day's Agenda/Activities/Medications:

Dr. Appointments/Treatments/Therapies:

Bedtime Thoughts:

Date _____

Great Day

Good Morning, Fighters

Every morning we have a choice to make... will today be a great day... a good day... a whatever day or a bad day... I know it seems obvious... but then why do we have bad days... I know we sometimes hope for a great day but it turns out to be a tough one... or we wake up in a crappy mood and our day turns into a good one... this isn't the norm... a majority of the time it comes down to how we think... if we really think and believe we are going to have a great day we probably will...

What a great day entails:

A great day is what we strive for... what we hope for... what we fight for...

We must fight through the morning pain and the side-effects of treatment...

We must fight the mental and emotional pain that this disease puts on us...

We must realize how much of what weighs us down is not ours to carry...

We need to modify our outside influences...

We cannot be pushed around by the fear and negativity of others...

Who decides what a great day is, "we do"... who sets the parameters of what a great day is, "we do"...

We must lead by example... be led by our dreams... be the leader of our destiny... we change our day with our attitude... help others with our gratitude... we blaze our own trail to triumph... we build our own highway to happiness... we are the masters of our own thoughts...

Today is up to us... not the people ... places and things that surround us... the intangibles not the tangibles define who we are...

"My friends, your day is now up to you."

Then your light will break forth; like the dawn your healing will quickly appear and your righteousness will go before you; the glory of God will be in your rear guard and when you call out the

> Lord will answer you. you will cry for help and God will say, "Here I am, my child."
> Isaiah 58:8-9

Date _____
Great Day – Comments

Allen Tan (Cancer Survivors Network)
Make each day great. Great inspiration.

Alice Barker Goodson (Survivors of Head and Neck Cancer)
Wow... well thank you for that powerful word. I needed to hear this... this morning.

Kerry Fielos (Head and Neck/Oral Cancer Chat and Support)
It took a push to get me out of bed this morning. Thank you for the encouragement.

Morning Thoughts:

Day's Agenda/Activities/Medications:

Dr. Appointments/Treatments/Therapies:

Bedtime Thoughts:

Date _____
The Day

Good Morning, Warriors

I will never forget the day I walked into my doctor's office and he looked into my eyes (I could see the answer in his eyes before he said a word)... and then he said those horrible indescribable 5 words: "Unfortunately, David, you have cancer"... those 5 words would forever change my life... I began to sweat... my heart beat double time... my stomach dropped... my head began to spin... my thoughts racing... I looked at my wife as a tear rolled down her cheek and I saw utter fear in her eyes...

I asked the doctor (as I'm sure we all did) those 3 words: "Are you sure"... he said "Yes"... I then asked the hardest question I have asked in my entire life: "What's next"... as the doctor began unfolding the next steps I tried to listen but I could not hear... my mind was a jigsaw puzzle... I lost a piece of myself that day... but I now use that day as motivation... I have actually gained more pieces than I lost... I may look different... I may talk different... I may eat different... hell, I am different...

But I have gained strength I never knew I had... I am now a more accepting and gentler person... I see life through a different lens... a lens of compassion... hope and patience... I look at my life with gratitude... do I have bad days... you bet I do... do I have days where I just want to lie in bed and shut out the world... you bet I do...

But with each day I awake I say a simple prayer... "God, thank you for making me and Jesus, thank you for saving me"... and I get out of bed and make the most of the day that I have been gifted...

> *The Lord is my rock, my fortress and my savior;*
> *my God is my rock in whom I find protection.*
> *He is my shield, the power that saves me and*
> *is my place of safety every day.*
> *Psalm 18:2*

Date _____
The Day – Comments

Elaine Lane (Cancer Support Group)
Your words give me understanding of my struggle. I love myself more.

Rija Jelas (Head and Neck/Oral Cancer Chat and Support)
This brought me to tears. This is amazing... amazing words...

Pat Eames (Head and Neck/Oral Cancer Chat and Support)
There you go again bringing tears to my eyes. Your spirit is so gentle.

Morning Thoughts:

Day's Agenda/Activities/Medications:

Dr. Appointments/Treatments/Therapies:

Bedtime Thoughts:

Date _____
Memories
Good Morning, Fighters

There are certain memories in our lives that will never fade... memories that are vivid and will be with us forever... some we would rather not remember... others we hope to never forget... this is my memory of the surgery... it is one of the few memories that encompasses both: my morning begins with anticipation ... not much sleep from the night before... thinking about how my life will change today... I've talked and planned with so many doctors... nurses and specialists that they become one... the multitude of tests has desensitized me to the entire process. it's amazing when you're fighting for your life how important the details become...

Today is the day that will change my life forever... while driving to the hospital I watched people living their normal lives oblivious to how blessed they are... the hospital loomed in front of me... a giant box filled with hope and courage... as we pulled into the parking lot I was blinded by the morning sun dancing off of the windshields... as I approached the main door it opened as if on cue by an invisible door man with a wink and a smile... I crossed the threshold thinking my new life is about to begin... as the elevator went up so did my anxiety ... as I walked down the hall to surgery I was surrounded by superheroes... they are all exhausted but still managed a welcoming smile... the plan has been agreed to and is being carried out... I summon the courage to get through the next minute and springboard into the future... I am undergoing a 15-hour surgery that will change me physically... psychologically and emotionally as to who I will be when I awake... as I'm being prepped for surgery the nurses must all have doctorates in psychology for the way they made me feel at ease... as I am wheeled into the or I think to myself... this is it... I have hope for the future... the surgeons saunter into the room and go over a few last details with me ... I am holding it together... a wise man once told me, "Life defines us not only by what we do but what we don't do as well"... I am afraid but relieved at the same time because I am ridding my body of this disease... the anesthesiologist tries to comfort me... he puts the mask on and instructs me to count backward from 10... I remember 4 but not 3 and 2 will change my life forever...

You will go out in joy and be led forth in peace; the mountains and hills will burst into song before you, and all the trees of the field will clap their hands.
Isaiah 55:12

Date _____

Memories – Comments

Ana Maria Esalona buna (Survivors of Tongue Cancer)
It's not been easy but thank you for this.

Ana Luise Hartman (Head and Neck/Oral Cancer Chat and Support)
God bless you and your words.

Lucy Vozzella Carlson (Head and Neck/Oral Cancer Chat and Support)
God has blessed you with a gift.

 Morning Thoughts:

Day's Agenda/Activities/Medications:

Dr. Appointments/Treatments/Therapies:

Bedtime Thoughts:

Date _____

Thank You, Lord

Good Morning, Fighters

I want to tell that one person... that one being... that one soul... that one some-one who feels lost right now... who doesn't know if they can make it another day... I know you are tired and exhausted... that you are frustrated and fed up... you want to shut it all out... you want to hide from this disease and how it affects your life... you are close to your breaking point (I've been there... I understand).

(Stop... take a deep breath... clear your mind.)

You've got this...

Life is about acceptance and a journey of knowledge and enlightenment... it's about being a positive force of nature... it is not about shutting down and being angry and hiding from the reality of our lives... once we are able to accept our circumstances life becomes so much clearer... easier to handle... ..we can begin to live again... let's give ourselves the permission to be the brightest light in the room... to be someone that friends and family look up to... not feel sorry for... to be someone others can draw strength from, not cry over... God made us to live a life of hope and inspiration... not shame and blame... a life of strength and courage... not weakness and fear...

I know for a fact that none of us want to define who we are by lying in bed all day feeling sorry for ourselves... being pissed off at the world... disappointed in who we are... disengaged from life... (that's not who we are)... we have so much life that will benefit the world around us... to make a brighter day for those we love... to dream for a better tomorrow... to fight for another day...

So get up and get out and be you!!!

When life is great say, 'Thank you, Lord.' When life is tough say, 'Thank you, Lord.'

> *Every moment in between say, 'Thank you, Lord.'*
> *And my Lord our God show us his approval and make*
> *our efforts successful. Yes, make our efforts successful.*
> *Psalm 90:17*

Date _____
Thank You, Lord – Comments

Linda Nardell (Head and Neck/Oral Cancer Chat and Support)
Your words make me feel blessed to live another day. Thank you.

Amy Springer (Head and Neck/Oral Cancer Chat and Support)
Thank you... I am at the beginning of my journey but your words are already helping me.

Sue Crittendon Jackson (Head and Neck/Oral Cancer Chat and Support)
I needed this today. Your words touch my heart and encourage me. Thank you.

Morning Thoughts:

Day's Agenda/Activities/Medications:

Dr. Appointments/Treatments/Therapies:

Bedtime Thoughts:

Date _____

Back to Reality

Good Morning, Fighters

On this fine morning my eyes are opening to a new day... a day of wonder... a day of grace... a day to embrace... a day to impact... a day to shine... coffee is great... furbabies are great... my wife and caregiver is great... my attitude is dialed in... I feel strong... I feel motivated ... I will succeed... my heart is beating... the blood is flowing... I tell cancer I will beat you... I tell cancer to go away because I am strong... I am courageous ... I am resilient... wouldn't it be great to wake up every day with this perspective... lol...now back to reality ...

Cancer is bitterness... it is ugly... it will try to beat you down... steal your sleep... steal your hunger... steal your life... it will scar us both mentally and physically... cancer will try to control our lives and who we are... cancer is a beast...

We fight our cancer with 3 long-time treatments... surgery... radiation and chemo... but are these treatments enough??? Hell no... yes, these are necessary but alone they are not enough... we beat this disease by enduring these treatments but we must also have courage... faith... hope ... a kick-butt attitude ... and a will to win... there is nothing we can't do if we have the will to do it... people do incredible things every day... miracles happen for those who choose to fight... today let's do everything we can to accomplish the impossible... my friends, the difference between being a victim and a survivor is very small... we must never let anyone tell us what we can accomplish or let them dictate our future... if your doctor tells you you have weeks... a month... 6 months... a year or whatever time frame to live... you simply tell that doctor respectfully that you will decide your fate, not him...

My friends, we decide if we are going to be angry... petulant and pissed at the world... to live in the dark and play the blame game... or... we can be positive... optimistic... impactful and happy... yes, warriors... we have cancer but that just means that we will be a cancer survivor... now that's the attitude, my friends... with the right attitude anything is possible...

For all of God's promises have been fulfilled in Jesus Christ
with a resounding yes. Thank you, my Lord, for hearing the
cries in my heart and answering with love.
2 Corinthians 1:20

Date _____

Back to Reality – Comments

Dana Kumcrow (Survivors of Tongue Cancer)
Thank you. I needed this today. You helped me get back on track.

Sherry Miller (Survivors of Head and Neck Cancer)
Yes, yes, yes. I love this. I am grateful.

Brenda Ubelhor (Cancer Support Group)
You always put into words what I think and want to say. Thank you.

Morning Thoughts:

Day's Agenda/Activities/Medications:

Dr. Appointments/Treatments/Therapies:

Bedtime Thoughts:

Date _____

Cancer Saved My Life

Good Morning, Fighters

I'm going to bare my soul to you, my friends... I believe it is necessary that I share this part of my story ... a part of who I was... to help others trying to make sense of it all... trying to find the why in all of this...

Here is how cancer saved my life:

Before I was diagnosed and began my long journey... I smoked (1 to 11/2 packs of cigarettes every day) ... I drank (1-2 bottles of wine or a 12-pack of beer every day)... I ate (fatty and fast food every day)... I didn't exercise and I was overweight...

Though I did not want to admit it my choices caused my cancer... my choices caused my pain and scars... upon diagnosis I had the "Why me" ... "How unlucky I am"... "What did I do to deserve this"... attitude... but deep down I knew the truth... it wasn't easy for a while... I was angry ... upset... disgruntled... feeling sorry for myself... I thought my life was over... and one day I couldn't take it anymore and I screamed at God, 'Why me?'... 'Why did you give me cancer'... and what God told me next was amazing... and rocked me to my core... he said a simple sentence: "David, cancer saved your life"... wwhhhaaattt????? I was stunned and about to laugh and then it hit me like a ton of bricks... cancer did save my life...

My friends, before I was diagnosed I was on a path to destruction ... I was on a path to a much deadlier fate...much deadlier forms of cancer... or die in a car wreck from drinking and driving... but once I was diagnosed with cancer... I stopped smoking... I stopped drinking... I work out daily... I eat better... I lost 60 lbs... .my energy is back... not to mention the strength... patience and courage I've learned from the fight with this disease... the fight has also brought me closer to my faith... closer to God and Jesus... so I have to admit, cancer did save my life... everybody's story is different... my point in telling you this is to encourage you to look within yourself and examine your journey and you might just find that there can be something good in all of this struggle...

Stand firm...let nothing move you. Always give
yourselves fully to the work of the Lord, because you know
that your labor in the Lord is not in vain.
1 Corinthians 15:58

Date _____
Cancer Saved My Life – Comments

Dennis Eschbach (Survivors of Tongue Cancer)
Well said. Never thought about cancer this way.

Mike Maxwell (Survivors of Head and Neck Cancer)
Your daily posts show who you really are... helping others understand this journey.

Mallory Oestreich (Cancer Support Group)
Love your story. Your words are well worth it.

Morning Thoughts:

Day's Agenda/Activities/Medications:

Dr. Appointments/Treatments/Therapies:

Bedtime Thoughts:

Date _____

Will I or I Will

Good Morning, Fighters

Sometimes the sun doesn't shine and the stars don't twinkle... but that doesn't mean they aren't there... sometimes we may not want them to be there... sometimes we don't care if they are... but deep down we can always feel their beauty and their presence... sometimes we forget the beauty in this world even if it stares us in the face... like our beauty being hidden by cancer or we think it is... we are amazing people that cancer happened to... cancer frustrates us as we clench our fists in frustration as one hour bleeds into the next as we bleed from our wounds both physically and mentally...

We go through more emotions and make more decisions in our morning than most people make all day... decisions that will greatly affect our next step... our next hour... our next chapter... but we must always remember...

The tough decisions are usually the right ones...

The tough decisions move us forward...

The tough decisions hurt at first but will pay off later...

The tough decisions we don't want to make are the exact ones we must...

Yesterday is over... it's done... it doesn't matter if it was the best day or worst day in your life ... it's behind you... God has blessed us with another day with new hopes and new opportunities ... we must prepare for today...

Let's get our minds right... remember, it's not:

Will I survive... it's I will survive...

Will I beat cancer... it's I will beat cancer...

Will I have a good day... it's I will have a great day...

Will I make a mark today... it's I will set the world on fire today...

Just one simple change in our thought pattern can change our perspective which can change our day... and can ultimately change our world...

Lead me by your truth and teach me.
For you are the God who saves me.
All day long I put my hope into you.
Psalm 25:5

Date _____

Will I or I Will – Comments

Artie Zimmerman (Cancer Survivors Network - Head and Neck)
Your words make me want to smile and change the world.

Randy Higdon (Survivors of Head and Neck Cancer)
Reading this means I have hope for today and today will be the best day ever!

Ann Louise Hartman (Head and Neck/Oral Cancer Chat and Support)
Thank you. I needed your inspiring words today.

Morning Thoughts:

Day's Agenda/Activities/Medications:

Dr. Appointments/Treatments/Therapies:

Bedtime Thoughts:

Date _____

Go to War

Good Morning, Fighters

I am frustrated and angry with this disease... I have an internal rage as I know most of you have as well... so let's turn that rage into a positive force of nature... let it burn within... let the rage focus us on this battle...

«Let's go to war with cancer»

Our uniforms may be different... our weapons may be different... our tactics may be different... our battlefield is different but it is still littered with the wounded and the dead from this deadly opponent... every day we rise to fight again... every day we take the battlefield and tell cancer not today and then we fight like hell with everything we are... each morning we look in the mirror to see our battle scars and the bumps and bruises from yesterday's battle... we not only fight for us but we fight for our friends and family and our brothers and sisters in the fight... we fight for those that have gone before us... we fight for those that stand beside us... we win this war for those that love us...

We are at war with an unrelenting opponent that has unlimited energy and needs no rest... an opponent that steals our hunger to make us weak... steals our sleep to make us tired... steals our joy to frustrate us... most of all it steals our time... cancer is an opponent that continually beats on us and makes us want to give up... we will not give up to you cancer... because we are warriors... we are fighters... so let's close ranks... put our backs against the wall and come out fighting and swinging with everything we are... to turn red with anger and kick some cancer butt... we fight on... we soldier on... we will never give up or give in... we will fight you, cancer, until the end... so let's give it hell today, warriors... let's give cancer all it can handle... we have the strength... we have the courage... we have the will to tell cancer, "Not today, you will not beat me today..."

Now rescue your beloved people. Answer and save us by your power.

I will be victorious in my battle because you are with me even if it gets rough I will make it through because you Lord are there.
Psalm 108:6-7

Date _____

Go to War – Comments

Troy Gates (Survivors of Tongue Cancer)
Yep, let's go get them!!!

Jeff Strause (Survivors of Head and Neck Cancer)
Great words of wisdom and strength.

Julie Warrick (Head and Neck/Oral Cancer Chat and Support)
With your words you help me remember that I am a warrior. Thank you.

Morning Thoughts:

Day's Agenda/Activities/Medications:

Dr. Appointments/Treatments/Therapies:

Bedtime Thoughts:

Date _____

The Only One

Good Morning, Fighters

It's 3 a.m., my mind a whirlwind of questions and pain... I watch the fire alarm blink as if it has a heartbeat... I struggle with the dark and intimidating thoughts this disease brings... focus is difficult as I fight with myself for a reason to get out of bed... I look within myself for the courage and strength to meet today...

I begin to think:

Am I the only one who fights this hard...

Am I the only one who is scared of this pain...

Am I the only one searching for strength...

Am I the only one who has these dark thoughts...

Am I the only one going through these daily adjustments...

Am I the only one who is crying out in frustration

"Am I the only one?"

No, you are not the 'only one,' my friends... these thoughts happen to us... they do not make us weak... they do not make us different... we all go through tough times with dark thoughts... no, you are not crazy... these thoughts are not yours alone... we all have them... you are a human being... you are normal... (once I understood this my life became easier)...

We not only fight for our very lives but we fight for a normal life as well... do not be embarrassed... do not think less of yourself... do not let cancer pervade who you are... we must carry our cancer with hope in our hearts and love in our souls and carry it proudly and give those that stare at us a huge smile that says yes, I have cancer and I am a proud warrior and survivor... we must continue to train ourselves as warriors... we fight through every day to win the next... we are strong... we are courageous... so let's get up this morning and give cancer hell...and quote this mantra:

"We will never give up... we will never give in... we will continue this fight and we will win"...

Within your heart you can make plans for your
future but the Lord will choose the steps you take
to get there.
Proverbs 16:9

Date _____
The Only One – Comments

Jan Starr (Survivors of Head and Neck Cancer)
Thank you, I really appreciate what you wrote. Best wishes.

Bev Aalbers (Cancer Support Group)
Love love this article, thank you for writing this. Love this mantra.

Marilyn Ruedisvelli (Head and Neck/Oral Cancer Chat and Support)
You are turning me into a warrior, thank you!

Morning Thoughts:

Day's Agenda/Activities/Medications:

Dr. Appointments/Treatments/Therapies:

Bedtime Thoughts:

Date _____

That One Word (Love)

Good Morning, Fighters

There are so many of us hurting... not just physically but mentally and emotionally as well... we need each other as fighters and warriors now more than ever... we need our pain to be understood... we need answers to our questions... we need to find the why in all of this... we need that one word that can turn this all around...the word that will help us navigate through the sickness and pain... that one word that seems just beyond our grasp... as elusive as a fading dream.

My friends, that word is right in front of us... that word has the power of God behind it... it's a word that when said brings pure joy to the hearts of those who hear it... that elusive word is love... love is the pure essence of who we are and why we breathe... to love is to survive... to love is to be alive... to love is that tear in the corner of our eye... to love is to shake with anticipation... to hold each other in our proverbial arms and tell each other it's going to be okay ... love will never escape us if we are pure of heart and really listen to the hurt and pain of others... to remind each other that true happiness does not mean everything is going to be perfect but that we can see past the inevitable imperfections and see the beauty in the world and lives around us...

We can turn pain into gain... sadness into gladness... stressing into blessing... we all have the power to change our perspective with each passing second... we can help others see our positivity and optimism... our inclusiveness and hopefulness ... we can help others who are searching to justify why they must continue to fight... we can help others find their way and lead them out of their desperation... to help those that think all love is lost... to find that love again... to find their way back to the light... to help them smile again... trust again... hope again... to help them to love again...

As the great MLK once said:

"I have decided to stick with love... hate and anger are just too great a burden to bear."

*Love never gives up, never loses faith, is always
hopeful, and endures through every circumstance.*
1 Corinthians 13:7

Date _____
Love – Comments

Anna Maria Escalonda Bond (Survivors of Tongue Cancer)
As always, a wonderful message.

Valerie L. Cifelli Gregory (Cancer Survivors Network - Head and Neck)
Amen. Beautiful start to my day. Well said.

Linda Nardelli (Head and Neck/Oral Cancer Chat and Support)
Exactly what I needed to hear right now. Thank you.

Morning Thoughts:

Day's Agenda/Activities/Medications:

Dr. Appointments/Treatments/Therapies:

Bedtime Thoughts:

Date _____
(Live... Laugh... Love)

Good Morning, Fighters

There are 3 treatments to help us beat cancer... I know what you are thinking... surgery... chemo... radiation... right... nope... yes, we need these manmade treatments to help in our fight... but what about the 3 treatments God gives us every day... these 3 treatments are natural... they don't burn... poison or make us sick... they don't leave scars... these three treatments are live... laugh... love... no, I'm not the first person to put these words together... I see them every day on my living room wall... they are a perfect fit for our fight... the great thing about these God-given treatments is they are natural...they are very easy to access... they are free... and we have complete control over them... they are there for us as we wake up and are still there as we go to sleep... my friends, use them... practice them... overdose on them... make them part of your life... part of your daily routine... part of who you are... if you put these 3 treatments into practice the world and how you view it will have a whole new meaning... you will see life more clearly and with positivity... passion and perseverance ... put these 3 treatments into practice... what's the worst that can happen... You laugh a little... you love a little... you live a little...

> *But those who trust in the Lord will find new strength.*
> *they will soar high on wings like the eagles. They*
> *will run and not grow weary. They will walk in faith.*
> *Isaiah 40:31*

Date _____

Live... Laugh... Love – Comments

Michael Rajdi (Cancer Support Group)
Agree. Awesome 100%.

Yolanda Leonardi Khouri (Head and Neck/Oral Cancer Chat and Support)
Yes, your words lift our spirits and allow healing.

Cathy Robson (Head and Neck/Oral Cancer Chat and Support)
Yes, perfect words... live... laugh... and love...

Morning Thoughts:

Day's Agenda/Activities/Medications:

Dr. Appointments/Treatments/Therapies:

Bedtime Thoughts:

Date _____

Cry

Good Morning, Warriors

I cry like an infant when no one can see... I scream into my pillow so no one can hear... I pull the covers over my head to make an invisible fort... a safe place... a sanctuary... a club to which I am the only member ... I argue with myself... do I get up today or can I just stay in bed... if I stay in bed I won't have to deal with life... or the pain... the frustrations ... the weakness... the stares... the half-hearted attempts by well-meaning people trying to make me feel better...

I win the argument with myself and I get out of bed... I will tell others I'm fine when the pain is unbearable... I will have a smile on my face but inside there is turmoil... I have a pep in my step as the frustration consumes me... I tell others I'm strong when they know I am weak... I will try to be brave but I'm petrified inside... my friends, we all have these thoughts... we all have the same arguments with ourselves... when you have these arguments you are not different... you are not abnormal. you simply are "not alone"...

We are stronger than we think... stronger than we believe... stronger than we give ourselves credit for... strength can come in many different ways... strength can be physical... it can be mental... it can be emotional and intellectual as well...

On this fine morning as we open our eyes... let's also open our hearts and minds as well... let your strength flow through you... my friends, if you are reading this God has blessed you another day on this beautiful planet and in this beautiful life of his creation... each day God has blessed us with a clean slate... another chance to make ourselves better... another crack at life... so get up and get moving... make an impact today... I promise someone out there needs you... and more than that you need you...

Submit to God and be at peace with him; in
this way prosperity will come to you.
Job 22:21

Date _____
Cry - Comments

Kerri Hicken Madura (Survivors of Tongue Cancer)
Did you write this? The poetry of this is beautiful... I love it so much I want to hang it in my room.

Doricia Knowels (Cancer Support Group)
Thank you for uplifting my spirit this morning.

Danielle Marsden (Head and Neck/Oral Cancer Chat and Support)
You have such a bright spirit that can be felt through your words. You provide us with drive. I want to tell you how grateful I am to you. Thank you.

Morning Thoughts:

Day's Agenda/Activities/Medications:

Dr. Appointments/Treatments/Therapies:

Bedtime Thoughts:

Date _____

A Few Simple Rules

Good Morning, Fighters

There are many of us opening our eyes this morning not knowing if we can go on... not wanting to get out of bed or face the pain today will bring... there are those of us searching for the why in all of this... thinking can I fight this disease... can I beat cancer... some of us have just been diagnosed and are scared to death of the unknown... some of us are in the treatment phase... hurting... sick and in pain and thoroughly pissed off... some of us are in survival mode... some of us just rang the bell (congrats)...I know we say this a lot but nothing could be more true... wherever you are in your journey "You are not alone"... and you should be uplifted knowing you have brothers and sisters fighting right beside you... brothers and sisters that may have been where you are... and have come out the other side stronger than before...

My friends, cancer can challenge some of our physical abilities... but it cannot in any way take away what makes us human... cancer cannot control our minds... our hearts... or our souls... if we can fill these 3 human conditions with positivity and optimism there is nothing we cannot do or accomplish... all 3 together promote hope... and with hope anything is possible... to have a healthy mind... heart and soul there are a few simple rules:

Surround ourselves with positive people that understand and respect us.

Surrender to the things we cannot control, to beat the things we can.

To use our strength to climb the mountain and win no matter what it takes.

To search our souls for the wisdom and strength to carry on.

To concentrate on survival and find the courage to become a better person

Don't be afraid to take that next step... because that next step moves us closer to beating the beast... the next step moves us closer to our goal... the next step leads us to victory...

This I declare about the Lord: he alone is my refuge,
my place of safety and simplicity. He is my God and
I trust in him.
Psalm 91:2

Date _____

A Few Simple Rules – Comments

Jeff Straus (Survivors of Head and Neck Cancer)
Great words to fight for.

Chris Purvis (Survivors of Head and Neck Cancer)
Reading this makes me happy to be alive.

Kimberly Kurz (Head and Neck/Oral Cancer Chat and Support)
Thank you for letting me see "we are not alone."

Morning Thoughts:

Day's Agenda/Activities/Medications:

Dr. Appointments/Treatments/Therapies:

Bedtime Thoughts:

Date _____
The Enemy

Good Morning, Fighters

If you think you want to give up you haven't given up... if you think you want to quit you haven't quit... if you think you can't take another step you're still stepping... still walking... if you think you can't fight another second you're still fighting...

It seems we fight until exhaustion and then we fight some more... we fight the frustration of an enemy we cannot confront... talk to or reason with... the enemy that tries to steal our food... our passion... our life... our every breath... the sleepless nights... staring into nothing... our minds a whirlwind of uncertainty and fear... the roller-coaster of emotions that surface... it seems our life is out of control... taking one step forward and two steps back... no one understands how we feel... we lie in bed telling ourselves life is just too hard... even a win feels like a loss... (any of this sound familiar?)... you're just getting home from the pity party (lol)...

My friends, we all go through these mental and emotional battles... some tougher than others but hard just the same... it's perfectly ok to feel this way... to have these life-altering thoughts... it does not mean we are weak... it does not mean we are different... we are not on an island by ourselves... we are normal... we are now part of the warrior brand... we are now in this fight to win it... my friends, remember this... not "if" but "when" you beat this disease there is absolutely nothing you can't do or accomplish... nothing life can throw at you that you can't beat... no situation that you can't handle... no challenge that you can't rise to... because you are now a warrior... you are now with the elite... you are now a survivor of the toughest kind... you are now a winner...

> *What's more I am with you and I will protect you wherever you go.*
> *I will not leave you until I have given you everything I promised you.*
> *Genesis 28:15*

Date _____
The Enemy - Comments

Karen Panbo (Cancer Support Group)
Thank you. I needed to hear this.

Kevin Puckett (Cancer Support Group)
Thank you!!! This is awesome!! I always try to maintain a positive attitude but it is not easy!! This post is so much more!!

Adele King (Head and Neck/Oral Cancer Chat and Support)
Thank you—very well said and so bloody true

Morning Thoughts:

Day's Agenda/Activities/Medications:

Dr. Appointments/Treatments/Therapies:

Bedtime Thoughts:

Date _____

Apologize

Good Morning, Fighters

We must never apologize for our passion... we must never apologize for our fire... we must never apologize for our optimism... our positivity... our hopes or our desires... my friends, God knew what he was doing when he built us. he molded us in his image... he gave us a heart that beats with life... a soul that wants to love... a mind that wants to solve... and a beautiful body to carry it all... my friends, God did not build us to be soft... to be weak or to fade under pressure... God built us to withstand the impact of life... to solve tough challenges... to work through issues... when life punches us we punch back... God does not give us a good life or a bad life, he simply gives us life... and throws in free will and opportunity... we take it from there... we make our own choices and decisions... each of us has immense strength that we take for granted... each of us has the opportunity of faith in our lives... each of us has the capability of love in our lives... each of us has the courage of a lion in us...

God gives us all of these tools but it's up to us to learn how to incorporate and implement them into our lives...

Cancer tries to make us think we look and feel weak... this is simply not true... in fact, others look to us for strength... others draw courage from our fight... we need to use our strengths to make ourselves and others close to us better people... to smile at a stranger and help them have a better day... to spread that same passion... fire... hope and desire... to make this world a better world... to make ourselves a better people!!

> *Trust in the Lord with all your heart. Do not depend*
> *on your own understanding: seek his will in all you do*
> *and he will show you which path to take.*
> *Proverbs 3:5-6*

Date _____

Apologize – Comments

Ouida Cox (Survivors of Tongue Cancer)
Thank you for your comforting words.

Sornya Karien (Cancer Survivors and Supporters)
Love it!!

Treva Downs (Head and Neck/Oral Cancer Chat and Support)
So beautiful and inspirational.

Morning Thoughts:

Day's Agenda/Activities/Medications:

Dr. Appointments/Treatments/Therapies:

Bedtime Thoughts:

Date _____

The UFC

Good Morning, Fighters

The frustration is so real, I want to pull the covers over my head and scream "Why me" ... sleep is a term I'm losing faith in... the pain makes me want to put a fist through the wall... my head throbs to the beat of my heart... I want to throat punch the next person who stares at me... I want to put today behind me before it begins... buck up, buttercup!!!

We are the UFC (ultimate fighters of cancer)

We are just as strong or stronger than those that fight in the cage... or ring... we must train our bodies every day to deal with this disease... our mentality to win at all costs is a must just like theirs... we both choose victory over victimization... positivity over negativity... optimism over adversity... strength over weakness... as we awake on this fine morning we must realize God has gifted us another day(... another round in the ring... so let's come out swinging, my friends... we can beat this disease... ..to have a strong mentality is a must... a simple winning game plan...

We start by doing what is necessary...

We progress by being strong and achieving what is possible... then we push a little harder and give this fight everything we have and we are suddenly doing the impossible... (beating down cancer)...

We continue to beat this unrelenting opponent until it is down for the count...

Why do you think we are called warriors... it darn sure isn't because we are weak... my friends and fellow fighters, it's because we are warriors of the toughest kind... so let's be the UFC (ultimate fighters of cancer) and kick some cancer butt...

> *He gives power to the weak and*
> *strength to the powerless.*
> *Isaiah 40:29*

Date _____

The UFC – Comments

Kate Fairbrother (Head and Neck/Oral Cancer Chat and Support)
Your words give me strength... thank you.

Daniel Pezzullo (Cancer Support for Patients and Their Families)
Amen brother.

Jackie Barga (Cancer Support for Patients and Their Families)
This brought tears to my eyes.

Morning Thoughts:

Day's Agenda/Activities/Medications:

Dr. Appointments/Treatments/Therapies:

Bedtime Thoughts:

Date _____

The Mirror

The mirror... something so simple yet reveals all of our complexities... a piece of glass that encapsulates our entire life with a glance... we can't pretend to be someone or something we're not... a snapshot of our psyche... it shows us the good... the bad and the ugly... what we see is what is... no bending the rules or lobbying for a different outcome... the mirror shows us the truth in a world of lies... it holds nothing back...

We can see every detail of the pain... frustration and fear... we see the brutal honesty of our situation... we see the change in our reflection due to cancer... we see how cancer affects us not only physically... but mentally and emotionally as well... we see the scars and disfigurement that now make up our new reality... we look into the mirror with the intensity of a lioness stalking her prey trying to remember what we looked like before... before cancer completely changed our reflection...

< We must try to look past what we see >

because if we look hard enough in that same mirror we can see a better and more beautiful person than before... we can see a person with more strength... courage and character than before... we are now a beautiful combination of scars and pain... a beautiful mosaic of our battles and challenges fought... we have had things taken from us but other things given to us... the look in our eyes may have changed but we are still the same person inside... we now see life in a whole new way... the mirror shows us every detail of our "new life"... although it's up to us to define "new"...

Our "new life" can be one of pain... excuses and blame... or we can choose a "new life of positivity" ... optimism... hope... patience... perseverance and potential... our "new life" is completely up to us on how we define it ... the mirror will always show us the truth... the truth is what will lead us to happiness... the truth is what will lead us to victory...

May the Lord bless you and protect you.
May the Lord smile on you and be gracious to you.
May the Lord show you his favor and give you his peace.
Numbers 6:24-26

Date _____

The Mirror – Comments

Willie Suarez (Survivors of Tongue Cancer)
Motivating post. Thank you.

Randy Higdon (Survivors of Head and Neck Cancer)
I choose your positivity to get me through the day...

Lisa Lewallen (Head and Neck/Oral Cancer Chat and Support)
You read my mind—unbelievable...

Morning Thoughts:

Day's Agenda/Activities/Medications:

Dr. Appointments/Treatments/Therapies:

Bedtime Thoughts:

Date _____
The Storm Inside

Good Morning, Fighters

As I listen to the storm outside my bedroom window... I try to quiet the storm within my soul...my mind skipping from one thought to the next like a broken record... I begin to question where do we fit in to the circle of life... where do we fit into life's scheme now that we have cancer? How insignificant are we... I know there are times when we feel all alone... we feel abandoned...we feel unnoticed... even invisible...and then a smile crossed my lips as I thought that it doesn't matter how many billions of people there are on this earth, we are significant to the right people...the people we care for and those that care for us... we are significant to our first loves...to our first childhood friends... we are significant to the memories we have made with others...we are significant to the stranger we gave a quick smile to...to the person we held the door for or held it for us... the person we said to "have a great day" as we exited the elevator...

People will come and go throughout our lives... some will affect us in a negative way ... some will disappoint us... some will have no effect at all... but there are others that will fight for us...love us through thick and thin... stick by us through the storm...some will even take an oath with us to be by our side forever... my friends, we are significant to the right people. We are a huge part of the circle of life... our circle of life... we impact the right lives...we impact family and friends... our significant others... our children and grandchildren... we need to take inventory of our lives and reflect on those we have helped and those that have helped us...we will then realize God has blessed us with so much...we are significant in so many ways to so many people... so get up, warriors, and let's meet this fine morning...we have many lives to impact today... we have many loves to love today ... we have many wins to win today...

Let God transform you into a new person by changing
the way you think...then you will learn to know God's will
for you which is good and pleasing and perfect.
Romans 12:2

Date _____

The Storm – Comments

Claire Latham (Cancer Support Group)
Thank you for your wise words.

Josie O'Shea (Head and Neck/Oral Cancer Chat and Support)
Love your posts. They have helped me through the last 12 months. Thank you so much for your words.

Krista Vigil (Head and Neck/Oral Cancer Chat and Support)
Your words of encouragement are awesome so thank you so much.

Morning Thoughts:

Day's Agenda/Activities/Medications:

Dr. Appointments/Treatments/Therapies:

Bedtime Thoughts:

Date _____

Symbiosis

Good Morning, Fighters

God has us face tough and challenging times to get us ready to enjoy the best of times... life is all about give and take... it's about push and pull... yin and yang... life is about acceptance and compromise... life in a word is symbiosis... to have a symbiotic relationship with life is the key... I don't care who you are... if you have millions in the bank... if you are the local hero... if you are a king or queen... president or prime minister... I don't care if you are at the very top of the food chain, you are still going to have problems... challenges... negative issues to overcome... we all do... God made us to fight because with fighting comes satisfaction... wisdom... strength and a feeling of accomplishment that fame and money can't buy... we have done something to better ourselves and those around us... God always gives us choices... I believe God's word for choice is free will...and lest we forget there cannot be good without bad... strength without weakness... love without hate... happiness without sadness... life without death...

We fight so hard to get on that road to recovery ... the road to beating cancer... right when we want to give up we kick it into high gear... put the pedal to the metal. hit overdrive... to fight with passion and anger... the only thing stopping us from reaching our ultimate goal is fear... my friends, there are many great things on the other side of fear... like passion... cancer hates that... like an optimistic can-do attitude... cancer hates that... to have the will to win... cancer hates that... so let's make a new enemy today... let's make cancer hate us... if cancer hates us then we are on the road to recovery... we can and will win this battle... we can and will win this war... so let's keep fighting, my brothers and sisters... we've got this...

> *Then Christ will make his home in your hearts as you trust in him*
> *so that I may know you more and more each day. Your roots will*
> *grow down into God's love and keep you strong.*
> *Ephesians 3:17*

Date _____

Symbiosis – Comments

Peter Schular (Cancer Support Group)
Amen... your good positive words are amazing.

Melissa Ann (Head and Neck/Oral Cancer Chat and Support)
My dear friend and fellow fighter thank you for your words.

Milli Beasley (Head and Neck/Oral Cancer Chat and Support)
Loved reading this. Thank you. You put a smile on my face.

Morning Thoughts:

Day's Agenda/Activities/Medications:

Dr. Appointments/Treatments/Therapies:

Bedtime Thoughts:

Date _____

Uncertainty

Good Morning, Fighters

Every morning we awake to uncertainty... that's normal, isn't it... what's normal anyway... we scream in frustration but no one hears... sleep escapes us once again... we think can I cover my eyes and disappear... can I pull the covers up and pretend everything is okay... will the world truly miss me today... will friends and family knock on my door... do I even want them to... a tinge of pain brings me back to reality and I begin another day... another day to face down the enemy... another day to become stronger... another day to inspire... another day to win...

My friends, we fight through more emotions and make more decisions in the first 10 seconds of our morning than most people do all day... sometimes we can get overwhelmed with life and our emotions so let them out... be happy to be alive... be frustrated at the fight... be angry at this disease... it's okay to feel this way at times... we all do... if you are feeling these emotions you are alive... God has blessed you another day... so really feel those emotions... it takes immense strength to get out of bed... so get up and get moving... it takes a courage second to none to fight this disease... so fight... it takes intense anger to beat this disease so get angry and beat it... don't let cancer dictate your life... you decide your life today... you decide what you will become today... it doesn't matter who you are... where you are... what color you are... what gender you are... what religion you are... how old you are... and it darn sure doesn't care about your political affiliation (lol)... this disease will test you... it will come at you... it will try to break you... it wants you to do nothing so it can rule you... my friends, we must fight... we must fight with everything we have and all that we are... we must compete... get off the bench and on to the field... get out of the dugout and swing the bat... let this disease know you mean business... that you are not afraid to fight...that you will punch back. it will not beat you today or tomorrow or next week or next year... you look cancer dead in the eye and let it know you are a warrior... you are a fighter... you are a survivor... you are a winner...

So after you have suffered a little while, he will
restore support and strengthen you and he will place
you on a firm foundation to help others.
1st Peter 5:10

Date _____

Uncertainty – Comments

Quida Cox Staley (Survivors of Tongue Cancer)
Thank you for your words of inspiration. They help me get through each day of my journey.

Hank Meyers (Cancer Support Group)
What a great way to start the day! So inspirational. Thank you...

Wendy Marrow-Kelly (Head and Neck/Oral Cancer Chat and Support)
You make me believe I can do this. Thank you for sharing your strength.

Morning Thoughts:

Day's Agenda/Activities/Medications:

Dr. Appointments/Treatments/Therapies:

Bedtime Thoughts:

Date _____
Human Spirit

Good Morning, Fighters

Our new reality is still in denial... we are angry... frustrated and exhausted... we fight an unrelenting opponent that we cannot see... punch or scream at... an opponent that abides by no rules and has no boundaries ... an opponent that attacks us 24/7 with limitless energy... an opponent whose sole purpose is to defeat us and make us question who we are... an opponent that is evil by its very nature...

This is where by the grace of God our human spirit steps in... the human spirit:

is one of a fighter...
grows stronger thru adversity...
shines in times of darkness...
resides in resilience...
will lead us to victory ...
our human spirit will teach us;
if you think you are weak you aren't...
if you think you want to give up you don't...
if you think all hope is lost it isn't...
if you think God has deserted you he hasn't...
if you think you can't go on you can...

The human spirit our very soul is made of immense strength... sometimes we have to dig deep to tap into it but it is there, my friends... we are stronger than we can comprehend... the human spirit has been our mechanism of survival for thousands of years... we must find that spirit it is within us and will lead us to the truth... our strength and our happiness... cancer is no match for the human spirit... cancer is no match for a warrior... cancer is no match for a survivor... cancer is no match for a winner... cancer is no match for you...

"For I know the plans I have for you," says the Lord. "They are plans for good and not disaster to give you a future and hope and the strength of the human spirit."
Jeremiah 29:11

Date _____
Human Spirit – Comments

Kim Gentile (Head and Neck/Oral Cancer Chat and Support)
As I read this I know I am so much stronger than I think... it makes it worth the fight. Reading this makes victory sweet. Thank you.

Lucy Vozzella (Head and Neck/Oral Cancer Chat and Support)
Thank you my friend. Your inspiration is always the best medicine to help me start my day.

Krista Vigil (Head and Neck/Oral Cancer Chat and Support)
Love this. This narrative is strong and gives me hope.

Morning Thoughts:

Day's Agenda/Activities/Medications:

Dr. Appointments/Treatments/Therapies:

Bedtime Thoughts:

Date _____

The Rule

Good Morning, Fighters

To give up is the rule...to survive is the exception... to lose is the rule... to fight is the exception... we are the exception... we are extraordinary... exceptional individuals to rise and fight this disease like we do... we tap into a strength others will never understand ... we embrace a courage that others cannot fathom... we have resiliency to fight this disease that others cannot imagine... it brings a tear to my eye thinking about what we go through to survive another day... the strength we have to do common chores... to go to the market... to run errands... to work... to take care of family and friends in our time of pain... we must look within ourselves and be proud of who we are in this fight of a lifetime...

We fight because that's who we are...

we are strong because that's who we are...

we are tough because that's who we are...

we are courageous because that's who we are...

we are a winner because that's who we are...

When we are going through our toughest times and facing our biggest fears and opposition... just when we think we are about to give up... at that very moment is when we are closest to our biggest breakthrough ... just when we think we can do no more... that is when there is a miracle right around the corner ... so never give up... never give in... we as warriors will fight this disease...we will win...

May the Lord bless you and protect you.
May the Lord smile on you and be gracious to you.
May the Lord show you his favor and give you his peace.
Numbers 6:24-36

Date _____
The Rule – Comments

Bev Aalbers (Cancer Support Group)
The words your write renew my faith every day. Thank you from the bottom of my heart.

Sue Crittendon Jackson (Head and Neck/Oral Cancer Chat and Support)
These words hit home today. Thank you...

Julie Warrick (Head and Neck/Oral Cancer Chat and Support)
I love the daily pep rally that you so thankfully provide.

Morning Thoughts:

Day's Agenda/Activities/Medications:

Dr. Appointments/Treatments/Therapies:

Bedtime Thoughts:

Date _____

Who Do We Tell

Good Morning, Fighters

Who do we tell that will listen to us... who can understand that we are scream-ing under our breath... that we are yelling in silence... that we are talking as loud as we can but no one hears us... who do we tell that the pain is so intense that we want to put our fist through the wall and scream into our pillow, "Why me"... who do we tell that we are frustrated and embarrassed about how we look... how we talk... how we eat... who will understand our anger at other people who stare at us... give us sideways glances... mutter under their breath or look at us with pity... how can others understand that every day we think about our sickness... about our pain... about why this disease is part of our lives... how we think about our new place in life... how we try to fit into our new role... all the while thinking about death...

We must believe in the human spirit... we have seen it... we have felt it... we have witnessed its power... each and every one of us has it... it's within us... the human spirit gives us strength and courage... it gives us mental toughness to beat this disease... every day is mind blowing on how actually strong we are... on how we not only survive but thrive... how every morning we throw the covers off and get moving... my friends, we fight way to hard not to live... you... yes, you... fought your butt off yesterday for the opportunity to live today ... to watch the sunrise and the day unfold... to impact someone else and show them the way... God has blessed us another day... let's not waste it... we are meant to do something great today ... let's also make our caregivers a part of our day today... tell them thank you and give them a big hug... tell them you love them and that they deserve it... today let's make one more person smile... give one more hug... tell one more person thank you... tell one more person we love and respect them... today let's just do <one more>...

Lord, I know you are right by my side. Your understanding
you keep track of all my sorrows. You have collected all my
tears in your bottle. You have recorded each one in your book.
Psalm 56:8

Date _____
Who Do We Tell – Comments

Donna Baker (Survivors of Tongue Cancer)
Thank you for being part of our day. Encouraging us each day to fight.

Ros Morton (Survivors of Head and Neck Cancer)
Thank you for your encouraging words... you uplift us sufferers and for that I am grateful.

Rebecca Corbitt (Head and Neck/Oral Cancer Chat and Support)
Thank you again... you amaze me. I just feel broken then I read your message and regain my strength.

Morning Thoughts:

Day's Agenda/Activities/Medications:

Dr. Appointments/Treatments/Therapies:

Bedtime Thoughts:

Date _____

Impact

Good Morning, Fighters

The rain wakes me up pelting my bedroom window... a soothing sound that calms my nerves... the storm outside has an unexpected effect on the storm raging inside of me... today is going to be a great day... each morning we summon the courage to fight another day... the smallest details that have the largest impact on how we approach the rising sun... the raindrops... a favorite song... listening to our partner's steady breathing as they sleep... a fur baby waking you up with unconditional love... mornings can be beautiful even as we fight... if you are reading this God has gifted you another day, don't waste it...

We don't fight to impress others... we don't fight for a big payday... we don't fight for awards... trophies... ribbons or medals... we fight for survival... we fight for family and friends... we fight to watch the sun come up... we fight to give our loved ones a morning hug... we fight for life's details... our fight is inspirational... others draw strength from our fight... our fight does not go unnoticed... others watch us with great intent... they summon courage from our fight... we matter much more that we realize. We profoundly impact others... each and every one of us will have a positive impact on another soul today... we will turn someone's life around just by getting out of bed today...

We are warriors... we are fighters... we are survivors ... we are winners... so get up and get moving... you have someone's life to impact today...

Seek the kingdom of God above all else, and live
righteously and he will give you everything you need.
Matthew 6:33

Date _____
Impact – Comments

Danielle Marsden (Head and Neck/Oral Cancer Chat and Support)
I salute you. Beautiful writing.

Chris Friday (Survivors of Head and Neck Cancer)
I needed to hear this today!!

Alice Barker Gounson (Survivors of Head and Neck Cancer)
Thanks, I needed this.

Morning Thoughts:

Day's Agenda/Activities/Medications:

Dr. Appointments/Treatments/Therapies:

Bedtime Thoughts:

Date _____
Mantra

Good Morning, Fighters

We cry out in anger but the silence is deafening... we scream into our pillow so no one can hear... we tell loved ones we are fine when the pain is unbearable... we have a smile on our face but the depression is palpable... we tell others we are good as the frustration consumes us... we put up a front of strength when others know we are weak... we try to be brave but we are scared like a child... we are excellent actors on an empty stage...

Does any of this sound familiar... have these thoughts or actions been part of your life... has giving up or giving in crossed your mind... have you thought, "Am I the only one in this fight... alone and isolated"... that only I bear this pain... that God surely wouldn't put anybody else through this... there is nothing worse than feeling alone...

The truth, my friends, is we are not alone in this new life... others are fighting the same fight... living with the same pain... experiencing the same feelings... thinking the same thoughts...

Other warriors have fought the same fight and won... other fighters have faced down this unrelenting opponent and have not only survived but have thrived... there are many other warriors that are waking up on this fine morning having to make the same decisions as you... knowing and understanding that you are not alone lifts a heavy burden...

That's why we have a mantra in our world, the world of cancer, and that mantra is very simple but very powerful... our mantra is "You are not alone."

Nobody fights this disease by themselves ... there is strength in numbers... so become part of this family of fighters... become a warrior among warriors... become a friend among friends... we welcome you with open arms and we will fight this disease together until the end...

Do not be afraid or discouraged, for the Lord
will personally go ahead of you. He will be with
you; he will neither fail you nor abandon you.
Deuteronomy 31:8

Date _____
Mantra – Comments

Carl Hill (Head and Neck/Oral Cancer Chat and Support)
You inspire a great many people. You give strength and encourage others.

Alice Harkness (Cancer Support Group for Patients and Their Families)
Please don't ever stop our messages. I am saving every one of them and when I a having a bad day I go back and read them. You are an inspiration. God bless you.

Linda Be (Cancer Support Group for Patients and Their Families)
I agree with Alice. Never stop your messages. Thank you for all you do.

Morning Thoughts:

Day's Agenda/Activities/Medications:

Dr. Appointments/Treatments/Therapies:

Bedtime Thoughts:

Date _____

Every Sunday

Good Morning, Fighters
(Mark and read this passage every Sunday)

Today is Sunday, our most precious day, also known as rest day...
to be one with God day...
to build a relationship with Jesus day...
to accept Jesus as our savior day...
to worship our creator day...
to try and amend our sins day ...
to put all hatred away day...
to recharge our soul day...
to fill our hearts with joy day...
to become a better person day...
to be there for family and friends day...
to hug our kids and grandkids day...
to love our spouses and partners day...
to thank and give love to our caretakers day...
to enjoy a day off from treatment day...
to impact those who need a friend day...
to relax and enjoy our life day...
Sundays form the parameters and set the tone for the upcoming week...
use this special day as a springboard or to set a game plan to start the new
week on the right path...

Sundays give us strength to fight through the new week... so rest... pray
and get ready for a successful week... a week with a new approach of hope...
gratitude and compassion begins... this week can be the very best week you
have ever had... it just takes the right attitude... a little hope and a solid perspective ... have a wonderful week, warriors...

*The Lord is my strength and shield. I trust him with
all my heart. He helps me, and my heart is filled
with joy. I burst out in songs of thanksgiving.*
Psalm 28:7

Date _____

Every Sunday – Comments

Michael Stevenson (Survivors of Tongue Cancer)
Thank you. Your words are a blessing to all.

Linda Nardelli (Survivors of Tongue Cancer)
A very special Sunday post for today to carry your inspiration all week. Thank you.

Kim Gentile (Survivors of Tongue Cancer)
Count your blessings day... these are always things to be thankful for and you my friend provide the inspiration

Morning Thoughts:

Day's Agenda/Activities/Medications:

Dr. Appointments/Treatments/Therapies:

Bedtime Thoughts:

Date _____

Life Speaks

Good Morning, Fighters

If we don't listen when life speaks we are destined to fail... we must embrace and listen to what life is teaching us... there are concrete lessons in life's nuances... we must try to meet life's challenges head on... when we try to go around... under or over life's challenges... they multiply... if there is a problem acknowledge it... embrace it and solve it... when we get in trouble is when we ignore... abstain or underestimate life's lessons... life is not fair... it doesn't always go our way... sometimes we think life picks on us... singles us out... gives us more than we can handle... sometimes we fight just to get out of bed... but as long as we have the right attitude and perspective there is nothing we can't handle...

I am not thankful for getting cancer but I am thankful for what it has taught me... I have learned that I have strength I never knew I had... to fully embrace each day... to enjoy the little things in life... to be a much kinder and gentler person... that others are fighting tough battles, not just me... that family and friends are precious... that life should not be taken for granted... to help others as I am able... to know that I am not a perfect person but I can try to be... to not judge others on how they look... that faith is not a fairytale... that most of life's challenges really are not challenges at all... it's our perceptions and emotions we must temper...that cancer can reveal the very best or the very worst in us...

We must try to use what life is teaching us and add positivity and optimism... and make a better life for ourselves... our children and our grandchildren ... friends and family... there is a true warrior in each of us... there is love in our hearts and strength in our souls... if we listen, I mean really listen to what life has to say it will say to meet today with a smile on our face and unbridled enthusiasm for what today will bring... listen to life with the right attitude and perspective ... this is what separates a challenging day from a day we will always remember with a smile... listen... life is speaking...

> *So after you have suffered a little while, he will*
> *restore, support and strengthen you, and he will place*
> *you on a firm foundation.*
> *1 Peter 5:10*

Date _____
Life Speaks – Comments

Bev Aalbers (Cancer Support Group)
I love how you write... with grace... thoughtfulness and to the point. Well said this morning.

Debi Terlop (Cancer Support Group)
Agreed. Your wording is perfect. Thank you.

Lucy Voszzella Carlson (Head and Neck/Oral Cancer Chat and Support)
Thank you for my daily dose of inspiration.

Morning Thoughts:

Day's Agenda/Activities/Medications:

Dr. Appointments/Treatments/Therapies:

Bedtime Thoughts:

Date _____

Superhero

Good Morning, Fighters

What is your superpower??

No, we can't fly around the world or run faster than a beam of light... we aren't bulletproof or invisible... we can't cling to the side of buildings or swim faster than a dolphin... we can't turn over a semi-truck with one arm... we don't have a magic rope or ring... we can't jump from rooftop to rooftop with a web or jump down 50 stories and land on our feet...

(We are superheroes all the same.)

We are superheroes because we are ordinary people facing insurmountable odds against a much tougher and more lethal opponent than any comic book superhero ever faced... we get out of bed and fight every day until exhaustion ... we fight every day in every way... fighting a disease that desperately wants to control our lives and who we are... this arch enemy that wants to beat us down...wants nothing more than to erase our epic story... to deny us another day... to steal our joy and happiness... to succumb to its will...

Each day we tell a new story... as we awake this fine morning God has blessed us with another day to add to our heroic tale... what will our heroic tale be today... will others listen to our story... will they draw strength from our strength... will our story inspire them... will it inspire us... ultimately our heroic tale will be to fight and fight to win... only we can tell our story... so let's start reciting our tale, my friends... let's tell it so loudly others can't help but hear... there is nothing keeping us from being a superhero but air and opportunity... so let's tell our story in all its glory... every one of us is a superhero... never forget how strong and resilient we are... we face our arch-enemy every day... and every day we kick some cancer butt... I salute each and every one of you... to my brothers and sisters in the fight... you are my superheroes ...

Consider it pure joy, my brothers and sisters. Whenever you face trails of many kinds. Because you know that the testing of your faith produces perseverance.
James 1:2-3

Date _____

Superhero – Comments

Debbie Dicker Ruscitti (Survivors of Tongue Cancer)
You help us face cancer one more day. Your words are always powerful.

Joan Childs Aston (Survivors of Tongue Cancer)
Your words are so inspiring. Thank you.

Julie Warrick (Head and Neck/Oral Cancer Chat and Support)
You are a superhero to me. I can't thank you enough. You have saved me.

 Morning Thoughts:

Day's Agenda/Activities/Medications:

Dr. Appointments/Treatments/Therapies:

Bedtime Thoughts:

Date _____
Coward

Good Morning, Fighters

Cancer is a coward that hides behind chaos... as we look cancer in the eye it turns its head in shame... cancer wants no part of a fighter... cancer hates fighters... cancer hates positivity and optimism but thrives on negativity and anger... cancer hates new beginnings... bringing us to today... today is a new beginning ... a beginning of new hopes and dreams of new aspirations and in-spirations... the beginning of new goals with a new outlook... a new choice... there are blessings all around us if we just open our eyes and see the beauty of a new day... my friends, we must also open our hearts and minds... fighting this disease makes our choices in people and relationships vital... people will come and go in our lifetime... some will have a positive impact and some a negative one... life will put us in relationships and situations that will impact us positively and negatively as well... we must be wise in who and what we fight for... we must hold on to those people and relationships that make us stronger, not weaker ... that give us hope, not sorrow... that make our lives sim-pler, not more chaotic... that build us up, not tear us down... there is one person that we must get right with before anything else is possible and that person is in the mirror... this person will be by your side 24/7/365... knows your deepest secrets and your every thought... who will be beside you through thick and thin... will have your back when no one else is around... get things right with that person and pieces will fall back into place... when we believe in ourselves others will believe in us also.

God, thank you for us...

A short prayer to start our day: "God, thank you for giving me the strength to fight this disease... a strength that makes me a better person and gives me a better life because of it... not in spite of it."

Don't worry about anything; instead pray about everything. Tell God what you need and thank him for all he has done. Then you will experience God's peace which exceeds our understanding. His peace will guard our hearts and minds as you live in Jesus Christ.

Be careful for nothing; but in everything in prayer and supplication with thanksgiving let your requests be made known unto God. And the peace of God, which passeth all understanding, shall keep your hearts and minds through Christ Jesus.
Philippians 4:6-7

Date _____
Coward – Comments

Kristie Leeman (Survivors of Tongue Cancer)
Thank you. I needed to read this.

Kathy Joann Eddins (Head and Neck/Oral Cancer Chat and Support)
Thank you for inspiring me not to give up.

Donna Craft (Survivors of Head and Neck Cancer)
I'm stealing this today. I know a few friends that need to hear this.

Morning Thoughts:

Day's Agenda/Activities/Medications:

Dr. Appointments/Treatments/Therapies:

Bedtime Thoughts:

Date _____

We

Good Morning, Fighters

If there is anything I have learned while in this fight it is that we are fighting a very tough battle... a battle that won't let us forget... we fight a disease that will kick you while you are down... sucker punch you... attack you from behind... it's an unfair... unreasonable... unforgiving... unbelievable opponent... we must always remember that no matter how bad... painful or disappointing yesterday was... if it was the worst day of your life in your mind... you beat cancer... you won... you have given yourself another chance to hit the restart button... you are waking up to a new day... a fresh start... there are fantastic... unforgettable ... wonderful... full of new hope... great days ahead... they may be tough to find but they are there... so approach today with faith and hope... not negative thoughts or feelings... your attitude and perspective will win the day...

We don't fight so hard to just exist...

We don't fight so hard to lie in bed...

We don't fight so hard to just be pissed off...

We don't fight so hard to be mad at the world...

We don't fight so hard to lose...

We don't fight so hard to be mediocre...

We don't fight so hard to give up...

We fight so hard to smile...

We fight so hard to hug those we love...

We fight so hard for the awesome days...

We fight so hard for sunrises and sunsets...

We fight so hard to enjoy the beauty in this world...

We fight so hard to live...

We fight so hard to make our lives worth the pain and frustration ...

to embrace the struggle... to impact life... to make a difference...

to leave our mark...

to show family and friends how much we love them...

that they are and I am worth the fight...

Give your burdens to the Lord and he will take care of you.
Psalm 55:22

Date _____

We – Comments

Elizabeth L. Walker (Survivors of Tongue Cancer)
Needed to read these words. Your words make the sun shine. Life is good.

Terry Longo (Cancer Support Group)
This hit me so hard—I needed to hear this. Thank you.

Michelle Colantuoni (Cancer Support Group)
Thank you... I'm fighting.

Morning Thoughts:

Day's Agenda/Activities/Medications:

Dr. Appointments/Treatments/Therapies:

Bedtime Thoughts:

Date_____
Forward and Backward

Good Morning, Fighters

My friends, our world is moving forward in some ways and backwards in others... we have a wider view of social media but narrower points of view... we have more college degrees but less common sense... more knowledge but poorer judgment... we have more experts but more problems... we laugh too little but are angry too much... we are on our phones too much and play too little... we are more frustrated and need to pray more... we've expanded our rhetoric but reduced our values... we love too little and hate too much... we have more and more technology and less and less communication ... we text more and talk less... we emoji smile more than we do in real life... we are going down the rabbit hole of hate more and love less... we are choosing division over unity ... acquaintance over friendship... wokeness over closeness... singularity over togetherness... status quo over happiness...

Today let's turn this ship around... spend more time with family and friends... talk more, text less... invite a neighbor over for coffee or a beer... smile at a stranger... build personal relationships, not just on Facebook... share a kind word with someone who needs it... remember to say I love you to those worthy of that high praise... be there for someone today ... realize your power...

Because we fight so hard don't forget to live... cancer is needy... it wants to dominate our lives... cancer wants us to think about it 24/7/365... it wants our full attention... it wants us to forget to live... to strain our relationships and make our lives a living hell...we must understand we are still in control...one thing we must always remember is that we are bigger and better than cancer could ever hope to be... we define our lives by who we are, not because we have cancer... we define our future... we define today... cancer is a tough foe but we are tougher, my friends...

They cried out to God during their battle, and he
answered their prayer because they trusted in him.
1 Chronicles 5:20

Date _____

Forward and Backward – Comments

Dana Kumerow (Survivors of Tongue Cancer)
Thank you. This was needed this morning. It helped me get back on track.

Wendy Swisher (Survivors of Tongue Cancer)
Great advice. Thank you so much.

Julie Warrick (Head and Neck/Oral Cancer Chat and Support)
As always you are right on point of what I need to hear. I appreciate your daily pep talks.

Morning Thoughts:

Day's Agenda/Activities/Medications:

Dr. Appointments/Treatments/Therapies:

Bedtime Thoughts:

Date _____

4 Questions

Good Morning, Fighters

We dream different dreams... we think different thoughts... we have different perspectives and visions... we perceive life differently... how wonderful is the gift God has given us... There are 4 questions that must be answered when fighting this disease... we must know and understand that we beat this disease by:

1) how we live 2) why we live 3) for who we live 4) the manner in which we live... we must be strong when we feel weak... be passionate in the mundane... have hope in desperation and fight when we want to run...

As human beings we are going to make mistakes... we are going to lose our way... we are going to play the blame game... we are going to go down the wrong path... we are going to have negative thoughts and feelings... we are human... we are all flawed individuals... how we react to those thoughts and feelings determine our outcome... the outcome is what defines us... it will define our day... our week or for that matter it can define our lives... we must always remember we control the outcome... we control what defines us...

Some may think cancer has beaten us... some may think they can't go on... giving up has crossed our minds... we want to pull up the covers and hide from ourselves and our lives... to shut everything and everyone out... it's okay that we have these thoughts... we all do at one time or another... it's in our DNA... if you think you are alone with these thoughts... nothing could be farther from the truth... you are not alone... many of us have been where you are and have come through to the other side with flying colors... we have faced the beast and won... so will you, my friends... after it's all said and done there will be one simple irrefutable fact... the harder you fight... the more you give... the more you believe... the greater the reward...

Dear Lord, may my heart always be forgiving
instead be kind to each other tender hearted
to help and to forgive one another. Just as
God through Christ has forgiven you.
Ephesians 4:32

Date _____
4 Questions – Comments

Adi Andvik (Cancer Support Group for Patients and Their Families)
I needed this. Thank you for sharing.

Michelle Blakeney (Cancer Support Group for Patients and Their Families)
Keep up the amazing job you are doing.

Monique Renee (Cancer Support Group for Patients and Their Families)
Love that. Thank you for the silver lining.

Morning Thoughts:

Day's Agenda/Activities/Medications:

Dr. Appointments/Treatments/Therapies:

Bedtime Thoughts:

Date _____
Different

Good Morning, Fighters

We came from different backgrounds ... we have different-color skin... we study different religions... different worlds... we have different socio-economic status... different sexual orientations ... we have different views on politics... different ways of thinking... some of us are older... some of us are younger... some shorter... some taller... we have different-color hair and eyes... we see life through a different lens... we are strangers together...

When we are diagnosed and the doctor looks into our eyes and says those words of infamy ... those tough life-changing words... we instantly become one... we forget the differences... they now seem petty... we are now the same... we are now brothers and sisters in the fight... we are now part of a family of fighters... we are now fighting for our very lives... we now have the same end game... a common goal to beat cancer... to rise together and crush this disease... to get rid of our petty differences... to lean on each other in this time of need...

I have the utmost respect for each and every one of you... how despite all the frustration and pain we continue to fight... how we meet each morning knowing we are going to struggle... how we get out of bed and take on today ... to fight like we do is extraordinary ... our courage is fierce like the lion... our character is as resilient as steel...our strength is second to none... when you look into the mirror this fine morning give yourself a hand... pat yourself on the back... give yourself a big hell yeah... give yourself the credit you deserve for fighting like you do... love who you are because no one fights like you...

Jesus said, "You must love the Lord God with all
of your heart... all of your soul and all of your mind."
Matthew 22:37

Date _____
Different – Comments

Bev Aalbers (Cancer Support Group)
So perfectly written. Your words touch my soul.

Mary Jane Cruz Nicholson (Cancer Support Group)
Always a good read. I try to absorb your positive vibes. I need your posts to re-cover my physical and mental strength...

Cynthia Breslin (Cancer Support Group)
Thank you for this. I was diagnosed terminal and that doesn't give you hope, but reading this did give me hope.

Morning Thoughts:

Day's Agenda/Activities/Medications:

Dr. Appointments/Treatments/Therapies:

Bedtime Thoughts:

Date _____

Our Choices

Good Morning, Fighters

How we approach cancer is our choice... sometimes this choice can be very difficult... there is nothing easy about this disease... at times we must choose through our fears... through our tears... through anger... through our doubts ... and sometimes we must choose through necessity ... every choice we make is life changing ... we must believe in our ourselves and our choices... our choices dictate our attitude... and our attitude will dictate our fight... and our fight will dictate what we are living for... what we are praying for... it's amazing what we can do if we believe in ourselves and our choices ... to those of you who have just started treatment or are in the middle stages of this process... to those who are starting to heal... to those beginning the process of putting your lives back together again...

There is hope... there is a future... there is a reason to be optimistic about what's to come... there are many of us who have beaten this disease and are now stronger because of it... we are running miles... lifting weights... riding bikes... climbing mountains... singing... traveling... we are very active in our new lives... we've stared down cancer and won just like each one of you can... your new life is there for the taking...

We have accomplished this new life by eating right... exercising... getting out of bed... taking our medications as prescribed... listening to our medical teams... thinking for ourselves... having faith in God... these are not easy choices... sometimes it's hard to get out of bed or to begin an exercise regimen... it takes belief in ourselves and our choices to beat this disease... our choices can make our attitude one of positivity ... optimism... hope and courage... think of yourself as a true life warrior... no matter what stage you are in you've got this, my friends... a little belief in ourselves and our choices will win this fight...

> *For it is by grace you have been saved. Through faith*
> *and mercy you are so forgiving. And this is not from*
> *yourselves. It is a gift from God.*
> *Ephesians 2:8*

Date _____

Our Choices – Comments

Paula Burn (Cancer Support Group for Patients and Their Families)
I just love your posts. You seem to come through when I am feeling down. Thank you so much.

Patricia Platt (Cancer Support Group for Patients and Their Families)
Thank you for this wonderful post. I needed this today.

Cindy Claffy (Cancer Support Group)
Thank you so much. You make me believe in miracles.

Morning Thoughts:

Day's Agenda/Activities/Medications:

Dr. Appointments/Treatments/Therapies:

Bedtime Thoughts:

Date _____
Ordinary People

Good Morning, Fighters

We fight so many battles on so many fronts... not only do we fight for our very lives but we fight physically...mentally and emotionally as well... we also fight everyday issues like everyone else... we fight to hold relationships together... we fight to pay our bills... we still worry about friends... family and loved ones on everyday issues as well as how our fight affects them... we fight insurance companies... we fight to pay our hospital and doctor bills... we worry about our futures and how we fit into society... we are anxious about our ability to make a living... we yearn for a normal life...

We are preoccupied with all of life's challenges and we still fight this unrelenting disease that simply does not care about our hopes ... our dreams... our hardships and happiness... we fight because we are compassionate ... courageous... caring and unbelievably strong individuals... we internalize and compartmentalize our challenges and issues... we wear our cancer for all to see... we are the very definition of strength... compassion ... belief and courage... we take care of ourselves and show others and cancer that we are in it to win it... we are stronger than can be imagined and we will never give up... or give in... we are the 'w' in win,... we are the 'w' in warrior ... we are the ultimate warriors...

> *Now all glory to God who is able to keep you from falling*
> *away and will bring you with great joy into his presence*
> *without a single fault.*
> *Jude 24*

Date_____
Ordinary People – Comments

Wanda Buchanan Mosco (Survivors of Tongue Cancer)
Wow this takes my breath away.

Treva Downs (Head and Neck/Oral Cancer Chat and Support)
Good cup of coffee an your encouraging words... what a way to start the day.

Diana Restrepo Copher (Head and Neck/Oral Cancer Chat and Support)
You have no idea how much your messages are helping in coping with all of this.

Morning Thoughts:

Day's Agenda/Activities/Medications:

Dr. Appointments/Treatments/Therapies:

Bedtime Thoughts:

Date _____
Complete

Good Morning, Fighters

Will we be able to eat today without choking... will we be able to take our meds without changing... our mouths are dry like the desert yet yesterday we couldn't talk without spitting... could the surgeries and treatments be worse than the disease... sometimes I ask myself that very question... we have chosen short-term pain for long-term gain... we have chosen the lesser of two evils in our minds... will the brutality of these treatments pay off... I pray that they will... keep the faith, my brothers and sisters... we go through more emotions and make more decisions in the first 10 minutes of our morning than most people make all day...

Our strength to get out of bed is immense... our courage to meet today is unmatched ... getting out of bed and walking to the kitchen is like running a marathon... lifting our morning cup of coffee or bottle of water is like lifting 100 pounds... getting through an entire day is like competing in a triathlon yet we are still competing... we are still lifting... we are still fighting... my friends, we are still in the game because we are compassionate... courageous and un-believably strong individuals... we are the very definition of a warrior... we are the very definition of a winner... never give up... never give in ... no matter what this disease throws at us we fight to win...

> *For we are God's masterpiece. He created us anew in Christ*
> *Jesus so we can do good things he planned for us long ago.*
> *Ephesians 2:10*

Date _____

Complete - Comments

Danielle Pezzuello Jr. (Cancer Support Group for Patients and Their Families)
Amen brother...

Cynthia Rodriguez Garcia (Cancer Support Group for Patients and Their Families)
Amen.

Susan MacFarland (Cancer Support Group for Patients and Their Families)
Great words. Thank you so much. You make me tough.

Morning Thoughts:

Day's Agenda/Activities/Medications:

Dr. Appointments/Treatments/Therapies:

Bedtime Thoughts:

Date _____

Win

Good Morning, Fighters

We must be stronger than our fear or we will only be afraid...
we must be stronger than our pain or we will only feel pain...

Cancer can change our appearance... it can physically change how we walk and talk... in some cases even how we breathe... it can break up our routine of daily living... it tries to change us deep down to fundamentally change who we are... cancer will try to change things about us but we cannot let it change who we are as a person... never forget that person you were before this evil disease tried to take control...because that beautiful person still exists... we may not be able to do some of the things we could before but deep down you are still you...

We can't let cancer make us question ourselves or dictate our self-worth... we can't let it infiltrate who we are or make us think less of ourselves... we start every day with a win by getting out of bed... every day we win little battles that when added up are huge... walking a few steps (win)... eating a bite of food (win)... going to the store (win)... making it though treatments (win)... going to doctors' appointments (win)... taking our meds correctly (win)... having a positive attitude (win)... a smile (win)... all of these small wins add up, my friends... and then before we know it we are winning the war against this horrible disease... so we must realize with every little thing we do... we are winning... we must recognize these small wins and gain momentum from them... to be proud of ourselves and our courage to meet each day and win... win... win... if we win enough battles we will then win the war, which is our ultimate goal...

We win this war with not only strength but also with love... patience... understanding ... faith... hope... courage and spirit... we just need to dig a little deeper to find us... we might even be surprised at the person we find... a new person... who can be even better than before...

May the grace of the Lord Jesus Christ, the love of God
and the fellowship of the Holy Spirit be with you at all times.
For you understand who I am and what I am all about.
2 Corinthians 13:14

Date _____
Win - Comments

Artie Zimmerman (Cancer Survivors Network - Head and Neck)
Again!! Yes!! You translate thoughts. You write what we think!!

Juan Sotelo (Survivors of Head and Neck Cancer)
Amen. Amazing. Have a blessed day.

Chi Ly (Head and Neck/Oral Cancer Chat and Support)
These words give me strength.

Morning Thoughts:

Day's Agenda/Activities/Medications:

Dr. Appointments/Treatments/Therapies:

Bedtime Thoughts:

Date _____
Word

Good Morning, Fighters

The word cancer can spark fear into the bravest of hearts... the word cancer is whispered on trembling lips... the word cancer is spoken in a hushed voice... the word cancer can manipulate the strongest of warriors... the word cancer changes our very lives... my friends, if we strip cancer down to its naked truth it is a six-letter word... the power cancer has beyond that is up to us... cancer is just a six-letter word like friend... strong... victor or winner... cancer cannot control our personalities ... our perspective or our potential... but it will damn sure try if we let it... it can be an unstoppable force if we give it the energy it needs... beating cancer is up to us as fighters... a few suggestions: we beat this disease with faith in ourselves and God... we beat this disease with belief in ourselves and God... we beat this disease with hope... positivity and optimism... we beat this disease with attitude and courage... each and every one of us has the tools we need to win this battle... sometimes we have to search but the tools are there... sometimes we have to dig deep to tap into their strength but they are there... sometimes we have to get out of our own way to find them...

There is one unmitigated truth...either we take control of cancer or it will control us... cancer is just a six-letter word... beyond that cancer has the power we give it...

You have allowed me to suffer much hardship
but you will restore me to life again and lift
me up from the depths of the earth.
Psalm 71:20

Date _____
Word – Comments

Karen Goode Anderson (Survivors of Tongue Cancer)
Stop making me think. Then cry. I just love your posts. Thank you.

Levan Knoerzer (Survivors of Head and Neck Cancer)
I love that. Thanks.

Renee Rogers (Cancer Survivors and Supporters)
So powerful and true.

Morning Thoughts:

Day's Agenda/Activities/Medications:

Dr. Appointments/Treatments/Therapies:

Bedtime Thoughts:

Date _____

To Be Alive

Good Morning, Fighters

Is it enough to just be alive... to just exist... to simply survive... hell no... we must also thrive... we get so caught up in our daily routines of taking our meds... cleaning our wounds both mentally and physically... cleaning our trachs and peg tubes and other necessities...we get tunnel vision on learning to eat again... to drink again... to deal with all of the pain and frustrations ... it's so amazing how we function without much sleep... how we smile at such a determined foe... how we deal with adversity... all the while trying so hard to put out all of these fires we forget to live... to be alive... so let's step back and take a breath... take a moment to find your joy... to feel the sun on your skin... listen to the birds talking as the day begins... to take in the nuances of life...

There is a big world out there screaming for you to come out and play... reaching for you to become a part of it... there is a new day dawning asking where you are... and wanting to feel your impact...today is a brand-new day with new challenges but also with new opportunities ... so embrace life and open that door and step out into the real world... draw in that first breath of fresh air and engage in life... meet today with fierce determination that you will give life a chance... give yourself a chance to be happy...

Ten ways to start the day:
1) If you are thankful...say it.
2) If you don't know...ask.
3) If you are overwhelmed ... breathe.
4) If you fall... get up.
5) If someone needs help... help them.
6) If there is a chance at friendship... take it.
7) If there is cake... eat it.
8) If you want to give up... don't.
9) If you want to give in... fight it.
10) What you have learned... teach it.

My friends, life can be so simple if we let it... we have the bad habit of complicating things when there is no reason... so today be simple... be nice... be kind... and do your best to be the best you...

Don't be afraid for I am with you. Don't be discouraged for I am God.

I will strengthen you and help you. I will hold you up with my victorious right hand. Isaiah 41:10

Date _____

To Be Alive – Comments

Mary L. Robinson (Survivors of Head and Neck Cancer)
Love this. Every day is a new positive attitude.

Peter Schuler (Cancer Support Group)
Amen. You help me walk above cancer every day.

Kittee Gath (Head and Neck/Oral Cancer Chat and Support)
Thank you. I am thankful for your wisdom that is given and the honesty that is shared.

Morning Thoughts:

Day's Agenda/Activities/Medications:

Dr. Appointments/Treatments/Therapies:

Bedtime Thoughts:

Date _____
Where We Are

Good Morning, Fighters

Some of us are in the beginning of this fight... we have just been diagnosed... our scans and biopsies have come back positive... we are now feeling overwhelmed... full of questions and fear... some of us are in the first phase of treatments... surgeries... radiation and chemo... some of us have endured all 3... again... we are full of questions and fear... some of us are in the middle of our fight... the not knowing and questioning if we can make it another day... the pain... the burning... being sick... bleeding... not sleeping... uncontrollable emotions... angry... self-absorbed... pissed off at the world and the unfairness of it all... we have good days and bad days... fighting is all we know... we push through because we have to... we continue to fight through the best we know how...

Some of us have fought through to ring the bell (congrats)... you should be proud... but the fight has just begun... we've all heard the old adage "It's darkest right before the dawn" ... right now is where this could not be more true... we now embark on a long road to recovery... we are not the first to walk this path and we are definitely not the last... many others have successfully walked this path to recovery and so will you, my friend... some of us have just completed treatments and are fighting the side-effects... at this point is where we learn to live... to come out on top in spite of all the challenges we face... we are not the first to make these difficult decisions and we are not the last... here is where we make the decision to lead a life of acceptance and fulfillment... or to end up angry and resentful of this life that now seems so unfair...

Every decision is completely up to us...

We fight the effects this disease has on our loved ones... we fight the financial hardship of this disease... we all fight to put our disrupted lives back together... piece by piece... we will rebuild relationships and bank accounts... we will accept our new normal from day 1 to day 1001... we fight the good fight and live our best life possible... fighting becomes second nature to the point where it's not fighting anymore... it is now part of our daily routine...

So let's begin the day with the knowledge that no matter where we are in the fight... we are winning... we are telling cancer "Not today... not tomorrow...

in fact, get the hell away forever" ... we must give ourselves the respect and credit we deserve... we are fighters... we are survivors... we are warriors... we are winners... we are some of the strongest people on earth...

> *Surely your goodness and unfailing love will pursue me all*
> *the days of my life. I can make it through any adversity*
> *with you Lord.*
> *Psalm 23:6*

Date _____

Where We Are – Comments

Debi Terlop (Cancer Support Group)
Omg!!! That sums it up. Thank you as always for your encouraging words.

Lucy Gregory-Wingert (Cancer Support Group)
Love reading your pep talks.

Dave Diaz (Head and Neck/Oral Cancer Chat and Support)
Hooah troop... from a Marine.

Morning Thoughts:

Day's Agenda/Activities/Medications:

Dr. Appointments/Treatments/Therapies:

Bedtime Thoughts:

Date _____
Chapters

Good Morning, Fighters

We endure the pain and we ring the bell!!!

Our lives are built on an intricate storyline... each of us has our own story to write of which there are many chapters... these chapters define us... they describe who we are... they give us our memories both good and bad... chapters we have written that make us proud or that embarrass us... chapters that evoke hope and pain... chapters we remember vividly while others are foggy and unremarkable... some we remember with a smile while others make our stomach turn... chapters that make us happy while others are just teardrop stained pages... chapters of strength and courage or ones of weakness and frailty... chapters we should not have lived through or ones we will relive forever...

Every morning God gives us a pen and a blank sheet of paper ... he then adds hope and free will so we can author what's next... what will be the focus... we must ask ourselves what is our next chapter going to be... cancer can take over the complete storyline or it can be one chapter... we are the authors of our own destiny ... we write our story... not cancer... we control the pen and paper and the words that appear... we could not control the beginning but we can darn sure control the end... my friends, get up and start writing... make today's story one that we remember vividly and with a smile... one that makes us proud... that shows who we really are... one that portrays cancer as a small piece to a bigger picture... make today's chapter about resolution and resilience... faith and hope... strength and courage... God has put a pen in your hand and a blank sheet of paper in front of you... so write, my friends, write...

(What is next in the story of you?)

> *Answer my prayers, O Lord, for your unfailing love is*
> *wonderful. Take care of me, for your mercy is so plentiful.*
> *Psalm 69:16*

Date _____

Chapters - Comments

Kathie Kauffman Migligccio (Cancer Support Group for Patients and Their Families)
Wow awesome words. Hugs and prayers.

Harvey Griano (Head and Neck/Oral Cancer Chat and Support)
Good morning my friend. Thank you for always inspiring me.

Terri Knudsen (Head and Neck/Oral Cancer Chat and Support)
Every day your writing gives me a new beginning.

Morning Thoughts:

Day's Agenda/Activities/Medications:

Dr. Appointments/Treatments/Therapies:

Bedtime Thoughts:

Date _____

The 6 Rs

Good Morning, Fighters

The 6 Rs to a happy day...

Rest... relax... recover... reflect... rejuvenate and reward ourselves for a job well done... to be proud of our fight and how far we have come... we have fought through yesterday and are meeting today with a great attitude and outlook on life...

Talk to yourself, you might like what you have to say...
Sing to yourself, you might like what you hear...
Believe in yourself, you might like where life takes you...
Trust in yourself, you might like who you are...
Talk to God, you might like what he has to say...
Sing to God, you might like what you hear...
Believe in God, you might like where life takes you...
Trust in God because he loves who you are...
God makes life:
so scary yet so precious...
so unpredictable yet so beautiful...
so hard yet so rewarding...
so mundane yet so exciting...
so crazy yet so normal...

God teaches us:

Our destiny is always within our grasp... our happiness is always within reach... living our best life is one breath away ... finding love is part of the human spirit... each of us has a heart and soul God gave us... so let's use them, my friends... share them with the world... there are others who need your strength...

See, I am sending an angel before you to protect you
on your journey and lead you safely to the place I
have prepared for you.
Exodus 23:20

Date _____
The 6 Rs – Comments

Peter Henning (Cancer Support Group)
Thank you for sharing... have a blessed day.

Terri Knudsen (Head and Neck/Oral Cancer Chat and Support)
I am grateful for your daily inspiration. You remind me of why I fight.

Pat Eames (Head and Neck/Oral Cancer Chat and Support)
Your words always hit home, and are very emotional for me.

Morning Thoughts:

Day's Agenda/Activities/Medications:

Dr. Appointments/Treatments/Therapies:

Bedtime Thoughts:

Date _____

Beat

Good Morning, Fighters

Cancer can beat strength into you or beat it out of you...
Cancer can beat courage into you or beat it out of you...
Cancer can beat faith into you or beat it out of you...
Cancer can beat you or you can beat it...

There is nothing easy about this disease... everything about it is hard... it tries to beat us down... tries to tap us out... it makes us sick... it makes us bleed... it burns and poisons us...it attacks us at our very core... it tries to fundamentally change who we are...

It would be so easy to give up or give in... to throw in the towel... to let it rule our lives and how we think... to make excuses... to feel sorry for ourselves... to let it steal our passion... steal our personality... steal our joy... steal our lives... cancer wants us to lie in bed all day... to not participate... to let life pass us by... ok, are we done with the pity party... (lol... any of this sound familiar)...

We need to look at this disease from a different perspective... a different angle... we need to see this disease through a different lens... a lens of strength... courage... hope and faith... cancer wants us to be compliant... it works to get in our heads... it wants to play tricks on us... and how we approach life...it wants to control us...

Let's pull ourselves together... get animated... get pissed off... show some emotion... screw this disease and what it tries to do to us... we are all in pain... we all look different... we are all in this fight... let's show this disease that we are in it to win it... that we are not going to simply exist... it will not beat us... let's show this disease that we are going to live a life that we control... a life with passion... a life with positive experiences ... a life we are proud of... a life we rule...not cancer...

We can and will overcome this disease... we can and will win one day at a time... we can and will have a productive day today... we can and will beat cancer... it will not beat us... we can and will smile today and live a life we control...not cancer...

God arms me with strength and he makes my way perfect.
Psalm 18:32

Date _____

Beat - Comments

Marilyn Ruedisveli (Head and Neck/Oral Cancer Chat and Support)
Who needs coffee when I have you filling my cup every morning. The best part of my day is reading your devotions.

Liv Thomas (Head and Neck/Oral Cancer Chat and Support)
I agree with you Marilyn. Going to bed with a smile on my face reading your words.

Pam Baranski Thompson (Head and Neck/Oral Cancer Chat and Support)
I am getting up and enjoying my day. Your posts help me more that you will ever know.

Morning Thoughts:

Day's Agenda/Activities/Medications:

Dr. Appointments/Treatments/Therapies:

Bedtime Thoughts:

Date _____

Easy Day

Good Morning, Fighters

For us to have the mentality of a warrior is a must... for us to get out of bed takes more guts than the average person getting through their entire day... for us going through treatments takes more fight than the average person can imagine... for us to eat one bite of food takes more strength than the average person can fathom... for us the difficulty in trying to communicate takes more courage than the average person can grasp...

But know this one and all ...

Do not think we are weak because we are skinny... do not question our intelligence because it's tough for us to communicate ... do not look at us with pity because of our appearance... do not feel sorry for us because we hate that... we are tougher... stronger... more resilient and patient than you can imagine...

I have a friend who is a navy seal... he tells me all the time how he can't believe what badasses we are... now this is huge... he said the seal mantra should be our mantra as well...

"The only easy day was yesterday."

I love this because it does fit our fight... there is nothing easy about this disease... remember... "the harder the fight... the greater the reward"...

Our strength is unmatched...

Our character is unrivaled...

Our courage unparalleled ...

Our attitude unabated...

Our will unlimited...

And our patience unmitigated...

We are simply unbelievable... ferocious warriors and fighters...

but most of all we are good people...

> *I will be glad and rejoice in your unfailing love. For you*
> *have seen my troubles and you care about the anguish*
> *of my soul.*
> *Psalm 31:7*

Date _____
Easy Day - Comments

Thirosha Govender (Cancer Support Group for Patients and Their Families)
Love this. This makes me want to fight each day.

Knox Zwane (Cancer Support Group)
Amen. Thank you so much. I love this.

Jamie Haddox (Head and Neck/Oral Cancer Chat and Support)
I love your morning inspirations.

Morning Thoughts:

Day's Agenda/Activities/Medications:

Dr. Appointments/Treatments/Therapies:

Bedtime Thoughts:

Date _____
100%

Good Morning, Fighters

Let's all be in a positive state of mind... let's all look at the front door and tell ourselves we can't wait to get to the other side...to gaze out of the window and be excited to be a part of the world outside...

I know some of you may not feel like it (been there - pity party)...some of you may be angry and resentful at this horrible disease (yep, been there too)... but some of us have done the math and the numbers are staggering... unquestioned and show how awesome we are as warriors...these numbers show strength... courage... positivity and resiliency ... congratulations, my friends and family ...

We have survived:

100% of our surgeries...

100% of our radiation therapies...

100% of our chemotherapies...

100% of our worst pain...

100% of our depressed days...

100% of our anxiety attacks...

100% of our wanting to give up...

My friends, we are all part of the 100 club... we are unique and elite warriors...we have won or we are winning 100% of all of our battles... our races... and have overcome 100% of our challenges...we are the champions, not cancer... we beat this disease every day when we open our eyes...we fight to win... I hold my fist up in solidarity to every warrior that reads this...we must keep punching... keep fighting... keep winning...

If you are reading this you are part of the 100% club... and God has gifted you another day...don't waste it...

> *For I can do everything through Christ who gives me strength.*
> *Philippians 4:13*

Date _____

100% - Comments

Higdon (Survivors of Head and Neck Cancer)
My friend your posts are the first thing I look for in the morning. You amaze me once again.

Kathy Joann Eddins (Head and Neck/Oral Cancer Chat and Support)
Thank you just isn't enough to keep saying but your posts speak to me.

lucy Vozzella Carlson (Head and Neck/Oral Cancer Chat and Support)
As always thank you for the inspiration.

Morning Thoughts:

Day's Agenda/Activities/Medications:

Dr. Appointments/Treatments/Therapies:

Bedtime Thoughts:

Date _____
At Times

Good Morning, Fighters

At times we can see no end... at times we can see no light, only darkness... at times we stare into the abyss... at times the world loses its color... at times it feels that our psyche is on the edge of a precipice ready to fall into oblivion... falling into the infinity of despair... at times hope has no meaning and weakness has no strength... we see the judging stares... we hear the fake sentiments... we are in disbelief at those who pretend to care as long as it doesn't disrupt their day... those that leave never to be seen again...

We face a world of side glances... sheepish smiles... the quick head turn...

We are aware of our difficulty in speaking while others carry on complete conversations without thinking... how we choke on our food while other enjoy their entire meal with a smile. how we want to throat punch the next insensitive jerk who stares at us... our rage at the seemingly never-ending pain...

Cancer pushes us to the edge... it tries to expose our weaknesses ... it attacks the very foundation of who we are... we reach a tipping point... a point when we must summon the courage to fight for our family... to fight for our children and our grandchildren ... to fight for our friends   ...We must fight for those we love and those that love us... we must smile at the frustration...we must rise above the pain... we must recognize our strength, our courage, and our resiliency. We must meet this new life and give it hell...

My friends, there is hope on the other side...we can still have a great life with the time we've been given... there is still time to have hope... to smile... to love...so let's meet today head-on with a smile on our face and love in our hearts...let's show ourselves that with the right attitude of optimism and positivity anything is possible... even a good day...

> *But I trust in your unfailing love oh Lord. I will*
> *rejoice because you have rescued me.*
> *Psalm 13:5*

Date _____
At Times – Comments

John Heath (Survivors of Tongue Cancer)
Your words let me know I've got this day. I'm now proud of my scars. Thank you.

Cliff How (Head and Neck/Oral Cancer Chat and Support)
Could not have said it better myself. Thank you, you saved me.

Donna Baker (Survivors of Tongue Cancer)
Your daily inspirations keep me going. Thank you.

Morning Thoughts:

Day's Agenda/Activities/Medications:

Dr. Appointments/Treatments/Therapies:

Bedtime Thoughts:

Date _____

Deeper

Good Morning, Fighters

Cancer goes deeper than the pain...
cancer goes deeper than the physical scars...
cancer goes deeper than what is seen on the outside...
no one is immune to the mental and physical suffering...
as warriors we do our best to minimize the impact cancer has on those
we love
as we fight to learn... we learn to fight...
stars cannot shine without the darkness...
there is no good without the bad...
there is no laughter without sadness...
there is no day without night...
we simply cannot have life without death...
so we must hold the hands of our brothers and sisters who walk the path
there are times in our fight when we think we have no choice...
that cancer is in complete control...we always have a choice...my friends...
when we think there is nothing left... that's when everything matters...
when we think it's the end is when it all begins...
when we think cancer has won is when there is nothing to lose...
when darkness consumes us is when we must reach for the light...
my brothers and sisters in the fight...
what we think is ultimately who we are...
what we think is what our future holds...
so we must fight for our brothers and sisters...
fight for those we love... fight for the future...
hell, sometimes a good fight is what we need...

Therefore I tell you... whatever you ask for in prayer...
believe that you have received it and it will be yours.
Mark 11:24

Date _____
Deeper – Comments

Mary Lou Manly (Cancer Support Group)
Best I've read yet describing us affected with cancer.

Cher Nery-Buffington (Survivors of Tongue Cancer)
I love waking up to these great words of inspiration and truth every day.

CA Andrews (Head and Neck/Oral Cancer Chat and Support)
Warrior, you truly have a beautiful way of putting in words how a lot of us feel.

Morning Thoughts:

Day's Agenda/Activities/Medications:

Dr. Appointments/Treatments/Therapies:

Bedtime Thoughts:

Date _____
The Big 3

Good Morning, Fighters

Up at 2 a.m. I'm daydreaming in the middle of the night... about the pain... the sleepless nights... what we endure... thinking how hard we fight as day turns to night and night turns to day we fight... as we see the sun we fight... as we watch the moon we fight... as we try to eat breakfast we fight... as we try to eat dinner we fight... as I was dreaming about our fight I began to think... not only do we fight cancer... we must fight how we communicate... how we eat... how we walk... and in some cases... how we breathe...

It takes everything we are to fight the big 3...(surgery ... radiation... and chemo)... those of us who have had surgery count every stitch... every staple... every scar... those of us who have had radiation try to soothe every burn... every sore... the peeling skin... those of us who have had chemo... shave our heads... wear bandanas to cover our sickness.

My friends... every stitch... every staple... every sore... every scar... every burn... every shaved head... every bandana we wear tells a story of strength... courage... resiliency and intestinal fortitude...that is second to none...they show that we have endured only what others can imagine... every one of us should hold our head high and be proud of every stitch... every staple... every sore... every burn... every scar... every shaved head... every bandana... let the world see them... let them stare...we should be proud of what we have overcome and where we have come from... my friends... we have been through hell and have come out the other side... stronger... as absolute fighters... absolute warriors... absolute survivors... absolute winners...

So is my word that goes out from my mouth:
it will not return to me empty but will accomplish
what I desire and will achieve the purpose for
which I sent it... I will hold on to your promises
you are always faithful.
Isaiah 55:11

Date _____
The Big 3 – Comments

Melisa Margaret Whitley (Cancer Support Group for Patients and Their Families)
You are absolutely 100% right. This is a beautiful post.

Emelda Candacy Benjamin (Cancer Support Group)
As usual well put together. Thank you.

Susan Knetzer (Cancer Support Group)
I am proud of my scars. Thank you.

Morning Thoughts:

Day's Agenda/Activities/Medications:

Dr. Appointments/Treatments/Therapies:

Bedtime Thoughts:

Date _____

Understand

Good Morning, Fighters

Can others really know what it's like to be told you have cancer... to be told your life has been forever changed...

Can another person really grasp what it's like to be pinned down to a table while a machine whirs around you burning you down to your last molecule... can another person really understand the patience it takes to be in a chair for hours while poison is being forced into your veins... can they understand how we wake up in the middle of the night in a cold sweat as the pain shoots through our bodies to the beat of our heart... can they really appreciate our scars and what we went through to get them... can they really understand how our nightmare has become a reality... the blood on our pillow...the pain in our soul...

The long answer is no and the short answer is no...

We must realize how awesome we are... we get up each day fighting to win... the fight is what makes us who we are... we fight harder in the first 10 seconds of our morning than the average person fights in a week... we persevere through more pain in a day than most will in their lifetime... we must recognize that we are warriors of the toughest kind... we meet each challenge head on... we don't crumble under pressure... the respect level that we carry is enormous... today is the day we tell cancer, "Not today... you will not beat me today"... and we get out of bed and give it hell!!

> *He that overcometh shall inherit all things; and I will*
> *be his God and he shall be my son.*
> *Revelation 21:7*

Date _____

Understand – Comments

Christy Ann (Cancer Support Group)
Made me have tears this morning.

Andrea Dye (Cancer Support Group)
Can you make this shareable. The world needs to see this.

Caren Yates (Head and Neck/Oral Cancer Chat and Support)
I look forward to your words every day. xx

Morning Thoughts:

Day's Agenda/Activities/Medications:

Dr. Appointments/Treatments/Therapies:

Bedtime Thoughts:

Date _____
Beyond

Good Morning, Fighters

Our strength goes beyond what is common... our courage goes beyond the pain... our resiliency goes beyond what can be imagined... our character goes beyond the fight... beyond how we must fight every second of every minute of every hour of every day...

How we fight to communicate... how we fight to eat... how we fight for every breath... how we face a world of stares... finger pointing and sideways glances... how we catch people looking with a quick head turn... how we sometimes feel alone when surrounded by others... how we fight through the pain and frustrations... how we manage a smile in the face of depression... how we push down the anxiety... how we get out of bed each day whether we want to or not... how we imagine tomorrow without physical or emotional pain...

We fight on... we push through... we give it all we have every day... we are strong individuals... we are proud fighters, not to be messed with or taken lightly... we are the UFC (ultimate fighters of cancer)... , we should be proud of who we are and how hard we fight... we must never forget we are an integral part of this world... we are all important threads in the fabric of life... no matter how small a role we play we are still part of the big picture... we can't let cancer steal today... we can't let cancer dictate our roles... we are the lead character, not cancer ... my friends, the more we engage in life the happier and healthier we will be... if you are reading this God has blessed you another day... don't waste it...

> *Your unfailing love O Lord is as vast as the heavens;*
> *your faithfulness reaches beyond the clouds.*
> *Psalm 36:5*

Date _____

Beyond – Comments

Dave Diaz (Cancer Survivors Network - Head and Neck)
I think it's fear that makes us fight. Your posts bring out the best in me.

Kathleen Bradley (Survivors of Head and Neck)
Your writings make fighting this disease easier.

Kerry Hernandez (Head and Neck/Oral Cancer Chat and Support)
I love your spirit. You make me a warrior.

Morning Thoughts:

Day's Agenda/Activities/Medications:

Dr. Appointments/Treatments/Therapies:

Bedtime Thoughts:

Date _____
Pain

Good Morning, Fighters

There are so many of us in so much pain... a pain we wouldn't wish on our worst enemy... a pain that goes far beyond the physical... a pain we never thought we would face... a pain that makes us question, "Is this all worth it?"... is there hope for tomorrow... should I even get out of bed today... the pain from the surgeries... radiation and chemo is unlike any pain we have ever felt before... as we soldier on and push through we feel like we have lost a piece of who we are... what is our new identity... how is our new life defined in these uncharted waters... we feel alone in this new world... (nothing could be farther from the truth)... there are many fighters who have felt our pain... many fighters who have had these same thoughts... there are many fighters who are going through or have gone through worse...

We may look different... talk different... eat different... hell, we are different... if we look within ourselves we can see life through a different lens... a lens of compassion... hope... resilience... patience and courage... we can shut out that sense of loss... pain... darkness... sickness and loneliness... we can begin to understand that with each passing second we grow closer to our ultimate goal of beating this disease...

Are we going to have bad days... you bet we are... are we going to have days when we want to shut out the world... you bet we will... are we going to have days when all we can think about is giving up... you bet we are ... we focus so much on the hard and challenging days that we forget to enjoy the good ones... days when we feel better than expected... days when we wake up in a kick-ass mood for no real reason... days when we can see real progress in our journey... the milestone moments of our cancer going into remission... scans that come back (Ned)... negative biopsy results... that we can eat again... talk again... sleep again... to look in the mirror and see ourselves again...

Every morning I say a little prayer that gets me started... "God, thank you for making me and Jesus, thank you for saving me" ... then I get up and make the most of the day I've been given...

And we know that God causes everything to work
together for the good of those who love God and
are called according to his purpose for them.
Romans 8:28

Date _____

Pain – Comments

Mary Jane Cruz Nicholson (Cancer Support Group)
So true. Reading this makes me feel stronger.

Bev Aalbers (Cancer Support Group)
Amen. Last night was tough but reading this makes me want to move forward, fight and not give up.

Linda Jeffcoat Amick (Survivors of Head and Neck Cancer)
There is always hope. Great post, love it.

Nancy Simpkins (Survivors of Head and Neck Cancer)
You've made me a warrior!

Morning Thoughts:

Day's Agenda/Activities/Medications:

Dr. Appointments/Treatments/Therapies:

Bedtime Thoughts:

Date _____
The Decision

Good Morning, Fighters

Let's get real...let's touch hearts... let's have a real come to Jesus moment about our lives... let's really unpack our situation and what this unfair... unrelenting ... uncaring disease does to us... how it tries to destroy us physically... mentally and emotionally ... we must confront ourselves about what cancer does to us before we can heal... let's take inventory of our journey...

We have been poked... prodded and needled until they can no longer find a vein... we have had cameras stuck up our nose... down our throats and everywhere else you can imagine... we have had more x-rays... MRIs... CT and PET scans in a week than most people have in a lifetime... we have seen more doctors... nurses... residents... specialists and therapists than we can count... some of us have to endure endless surgeries... some have countless stitches... staples and scars... we have been burned by radiation... gone through horrible rounds of chemo... we feel great pain... sometimes we don't sleep for days... we cry for no reason... we lash out at friends and family, not meaning to... the frustration of not being able to eat or talk or even breathe normally wears on us...

Life has thrown us a curve ball... life has given us the finger... life has looked us in the eye and said, "What are you going to do about it?"... what we do now... what action we take is what will define us... it will define who we are as a person and a warrior... don't let cancer define who you are... we must make a decision to fight... we must find our strength... tap into our reserves... deep down we must realize we have the courage of a lion... the resilience of steel... we must fight with passion... think how strong we are to endure what we do... and we are still standing ... still fighting... still surviving. we are still winning.

So let's rise and meet this beautiful day... make this day unexpected... make it a day to remember and not forget... make it a day you inspire someone with your bravery ... you and you alone decide what today will be...

Lord, you know the hopes of the helpless. Surely you will
hear their cries and comfort them.
Psalm 10:17

Date _____

The Decision - Comments

Guinn Nexsen (Head and Neck/Oral Cancer Chat and Support)
You should write a book for cancer patients. It would be a best seller. I want a copy of your book.

Cee Crich (Head and Neck/Oral Cancer Chat and Support)
Amen to that. Powerful words. Thank you for the inspiration.

CA Andrews (Head and Neck/Oral Cancer Chat and Support)
Your book should be given to everyone on their first visit when they find out they have the big "c," your book would give them hope that there is a light at the end of the tunnel.

Morning Thoughts:

Day's Agenda/Activities/Medications:

Dr. Appointments/Treatments/Therapies:

Bedtime Thoughts:

Date _____

Fight... Fighter... Fighting

Good Morning, Fighters

There is that one word that describes who we are... that describes our trials and tribulations we face every day... that one word that has become our calling card... that one word that has become part of our daily lives... that one word is fight...

We wake up and we fight... we go to bed and we fight... every day is a fight... every night is a fight... we try to eat and we fight... we try to drink and we fight...

We dream about fighting... we scream about fighting... we pray about fighting... we fight about fighting...

We have the heart of a fighter... we have the soul of a fighter... we have the strength of a fighter... we have the courage of a fighter... we have the perseverance of a fighter... we have the resilience of a fighter... every day we are a fighter... every night we are a fighter... we take the punches of a fighter... we have the psyche of a fighter... we stand tall as a fighter... we are known as fighters... we continue on as fighters... we never give in as fighters... we never give up as fighters... we fight through as fighters...

There is a common theme among us... an impenetrable truth... it's a code we live by... it's part of who we are as fighters... it is in our DNA... it's in our psyche... it is one unmitigated and unchallenged truth...

We fight... we are fighting and we are fighters of the strongest kind... we are tough... much love and respect for each of you... may you fight through and find peace today...

> *We also pray that you will be strengthened with*
> *all his glorious power so you will have all the*
> *endurance and patience you need.*
> *Colossians 1:11*

Date _____

Fight... Fighter... Fighting – Comments

Kerry Roberts Cooke (Cancer Support Group for Patients and Their Families)
Perfectly said!! Thank you!!

Rebecca Oliver (Cancer Support Group)
A warrior saying thanks as always.

Shannon Conners (Head and Neck/Oral Cancer Chat and Support)
Love this... awesome words.

Morning Thoughts:

Day's Agenda/Activities/Medications:

Dr. Appointments/Treatments/Therapies:

Bedtime Thoughts:

Date _____

No One

Good Morning, Fighters

God has molded 6 billion human beings and he made sure that you are unique... that there is no one on earth like you... no one who has your thoughts or dreams... no one who has your questions or beliefs... no one who approaches life the way you do... no one that loves like you... feels like you... cries or laughs like you... no one who has your smile... no one who fights like you... or has your will... power and strength... no one who has your spirit or potential... God made us very special individuals when he formed who we are... he gave us a piece of himself to share on this earth... he gave us a heart... he gave us a soul... he made us much stronger... courageous and resilient than we can comprehend ... we must talk to him and really listen to his answers... he teaches us that even when we are fighting this unrelenting opponent:

We can bend but not break...

our courage to fight another day is within us...

we can train our mind ... body and soul into a positive force of nature ... to win in the face of adversity ...

we must bet on ourselves even with long odds... pain has a reason...

sometimes we experience loss to gain strength...

but most importantly he teaches us a sense of self... to value life... to love friends and family with everything we are... to hope again... that we can beat this disease... that we can regain our lives and retain our loves... beating this disease is the hardest thing we will ever do... there is nothing easy about this disease... God has given us what we need to be victorious... we just have to reach from within to find it... the loftier the goal, the greater the reward... if you are reading this God has gifted you another day... don't waste it...

When they call on me, I will answer; I will
be with them in trouble. I will rescue and honor them.
Psalm 91:15

Date _____

No One - Comments

Pam Baranski Thompson (Cancer Support Group)
Thank you so much for your uplifting words.

Donna Carson Gerdes (Cancer Support Group)
Thank you for your words. You show me there is purpose for my pain. I'm not quitting, thanks to you.

Jamie Haddox (Head and Neck/Oral Cancer Chat and Support)
Thank you for the morning inspirational words. God has gifted you with a unique spiritual leadership that all these warriors look to.

Morning Thoughts:

Day's Agenda/Activities/Medications:

Dr. Appointments/Treatments/Therapies:

Bedtime Thoughts:

Date _____

New Meaning

Good Morning, Fighters

My friends, when you think you have exhausted all possibilities... that's when the fight begins... when you think all hope is gone that's when you find out who you really are... when all you can think about is giving up is when you give it hell... when you don't want to get out of bed that is when you must rise, when you think you can't take another step is when the true journey begins...

Before cancer I took for granted family and friends... hugging my kids... sunrises and sunsets...the beauty of a single rose... the deep love for the minuscule corners of life... before cancer it would take days... months... years and in some cases never to realize the meaningful things life has to offer... the bursts of how fantastic life can be...

Cancer has taught me to embrace those minuscule corners... to embrace life with the right attitude and perspective... I now understand the fragility of each and every day of life... the drawing of every breath is precious... I respect life now... I have learned that the little things in life that would take days or weeks or months for me to recognize are now instantaneous... to put my arms around the love of life that I had previously ignored... life has a new meaning to me... so thank you, warriors, for giving me the ability to change my perspective and therefore to change my heart and to ultimately change my life...

Be thankful in all circumstances for this is God's
will for you who belong to Christ Jesus...
1 Thessalonians 5:18

Date _____
New Meaning – Comments

Good Morning, Fighters

Michael Rajdl (Cancer Support Group)
Well said. You exude power in accepting who you are. You are unstoppable.

Penelope Michel (Head and Neck/Oral Cancer Chat and Support)
Thank you for pushing us to be the people we are meant to be.

Mateja Harrington (Head and Neck/Oral Cancer Chat and Support)
Thank you. Your words are so powerful and I appreciate them and you.

Morning Thoughts:

Day's Agenda/Activities/Medications:

Dr. Appointments/Treatments/Therapies:

Bedtime Thoughts:

Date _____

Worth It

Good Morning, Fighters

Today is the day that makes everything I've gone through worth it... the surgeries... the radiation... chemo and the pain are nothing compared to being able to see the sheer joy in my daughter's eyes as she found out she's having a baby girl... it seems like yesterday that I was holding her in my arms and looking into her beautiful little eyes wondering what she would become...

Just a short time ago I was ready to throw in the towel...I didn't know if this fight was worth it... I had gone to a dark place in my life... but I made a decision to fight with everything I am... I stared this deadly disease down and said no, you will not beat me... today is a day that makes that decision a great one... I now believe that God has blessed me for my fight... today we found out she is having a baby girl. I am being blessed with another grandchild... yes, this fight is absolutely worth it... my friends, I know there are times when you want to say screw it... you want to give up... you question if it is all worth it... I'm here to tell you it is...you may not understand it right now but you must fight... there are beautiful days ahead... these days make everything we go through worth it...

I had a 50/50 shot at survival upon diagnosis...I chose life and now am being blessed for that choice... as you will surely be if you fight... God favors fighters...the harder you fight, the greater the reward...so roll up your sleeves and get ready for battle because the day that makes it all worth it is just around the corner...

> *He lifted me out of the pit of despair out of the*
> *mud and the mire. He set my feet on solid ground*
> *and steadied me as I walked along.*
> *Psalm 40:2*

Date _____

Worth It – Comments

Noelle Salome-Cipriano (Survivors of Head and Neck Cancer)
Your posts make every single day a blessing.

Leticia Simon (Head and Neck/Oral Cancer Chat and Support)
Amazing post. Thank you!!

Diane Burton (Head and Neck/Oral Cancer Chat and Support)
Beautiful post. Thank you for the inspiration.

Morning Thoughts:

Day's Agenda/Activities/Medications:

Dr. Appointments/Treatments/Therapies:

Bedtime Thoughts:

Date _____

Bitter or Better

Good Morning, Fighters

Yes, the frustrations are real or are they unreal... the scars left behind to remind us... the burning skin due to radiation... the molecular changes due to chemo... we lose our hair and our smile... can the treatments be worse than the disease itself... the times we hold ice in our mouth to dull the pain... we use the wall to steady ourselves as we begin the day... our tongue sticks to the roof of our mouth that is dry like the Mojave desert... or we have so much saliva that it is difficult to talk... we look at that bite of food and tell ourselves that if we eat it we will get sick and choke... we eat it anyway and we get sick and choke... when it's hard to sleep as the pain throbs to the beat of our heart... we want to throat punch the next person who stares...

Does cancer change us... hell yeah it does, on so many levels... it can make us weaker or make us stronger... we can rise up or be beat down... we can feel sorry for ourselves and feel angry at cancer as we kick its butt... with the right attitude and perspective and add a little hope and a lot of faith... we can beat this disease... we can crush it... we can be proud... we can rise and not fall... we can accept this challenge... my brothers and sisters in the fight, we can win this battle... we can win this war... when you think you are at your weakest and most vulnerable you still have more courage and strength than you can imagine... this disease can make you a bitter person or a better person... it's your call, my friends...

> *Now all glory to God who is able, through his mighty power*
> *work within us to accomplish infinity more than we might ask or think.*
> *Ephesians 3:20*

Date _____
Bitter or Better – Comments

Annie Abeg (Head and Neck/Oral Cancer Chat and Support)
Thank you for sharing. You nailed it.

Judie Smith (Head and Neck/Oral Cancer Chat and Support)
Thanks as always for your inspiring words and an example of how we should all count our blessings.

Carole Smith (Head and Neck/Oral Cancer Chat and Support)
You hit the nail on the head on so many, many counts.

Morning Thoughts:

Day's Agenda/Activities/Medications:

Dr. Appointments/Treatments/Therapies:

Bedtime Thoughts:

Date _____
Today

Good Morning, Fighters

There is a common theme among us... an unmitigated... unchallenged... impenetrable truth... a code we live by... it's in our DNA... it's who we are... that truth is we are warriors of the strongest kind...

Today we push forward despite our challenges...
Today we own this disease, it no longer owns us...
Today we face down our enemy ...
Today we make an impact...
Today we smile...
Today we build towards tomorrow...
Today our eyes are open to opportunity...
Today we make this world a better place...
Today God has blessed us...
let's make today a day to remember...
there will never be another today...

Let's give today our best... let's give it all we have... let's live a life we control... a life of passion and love... a life with positive experiences... a life of gratitude and trust... a life we are proud of...

We learn from those who have gone before us...
we fight for those who stand beside us...
we win this fight for those who love us...

But I am trusting you, O Lord, saying, "You are my God."
Psalm 31:14

Date _____
Today – Comments

Nikhil Chhoker (Cancer Survivors Network - Head and Neck)
Bravo! Hard to beat this.

Pam Baranski Thompson (Cancer Support Group)
I love this and I'm going to save it and read it before my surgery. Thank you for posting this.

Kathy Joann Eddins (Head and Neck/Oral Cancer Chat and Support)
Your writings are so powerful.Thank you.

Morning Thoughts:

Day's Agenda/Activities/Medications:

Dr. Appointments/Treatments/Therapies:

Bedtime Thoughts:

Date _____
Battle

Good Morning, Fighters

We are fighting a tough battle... a battle with an unseen opponent...an opponent that doesn't pull punches... an opponent that will kick you when you are down... that will sucker punch you... attack you from behind...it's an unfair... unreasonable ... unforgiving... unapologetic disease we fight. this disease will test our persona... it will test our nature... it will test our foundation ... it will test our very soul...

We are going to have bad, even horrible days...we are going to have days when we want to give up or give in... there will be days that are so dark we won't find our way. days of indecision and chaos... days of heartache and pain (you are not alone if you have these feelings... we all do)...we must fight through these feelings...we must remember and believe that there are fantastic... unforgettable ... wonderful... happy... emotional... great days ahead...

We don't fight so hard just to exist...

We don't fight so hard just to live...

We don't fight so hard just to be angry...

We don't fight so hard to be manipulated...

We don't fight so hard to be destroyed ...

We fight to enjoy the sunrises and sunsets...

We fight to cherish the feeling of growing old...

We fight to reach for heaven and get grabbed by the wrist...

We fight to make our lives worth the pain...

We fight to make our lives worth the frustration ...

We fight to make a difference...

We fight for those that stand beside us...

We fight for those who love us...

My friends, we fight to live a life of beauty and expectations... a life of peace and love...a life that we are proud to live... a life that impacts life ... not cancer...

But now the Lord God has given me peace on every side.

I have no enemies and now all is well.
1st Kings 5:4

Date _____

Battle - Comments

Jerry Krause (Survivors Network - Head and Neck)
I woke up weak but after reading this I am ready to fight again. Thank you for the inspiration.

Jean Wilkinson (Survivors Network - Head and Neck)
That's the spirit!! We've got this.

John Heth (Survivors of Tongue Cancer)
Good day my friend. This message makes us pull ourselves up and kick cancer's ass!!

Morning Thoughts:

Day's Agenda/Activities/Medications:

Dr. Appointments/Treatments/Therapies:

Bedtime Thoughts:

Date _____

Things We Learn

Good Morning, Fighters

Cancer can teach us many things if we open our eyes and our hearts... it can teach us that we are stronger and more courageous than we ever imagined... that we are an imperfect mosaic of pain with victory... courage with fear... respect with resiliency.

Cancer can teach us we must embrace each day and enjoy the little things... to be kinder and gentler people... that friends and family are precious... that others are fighting tough battles, not just us... to help others as we are able... not to judge others on how they look... that faith is not a fairytale.

Cancer can teach us there is nothing ordinary about a fighter's soul... that it isn't often that life will exceed expectations ... that we must push farther and think faster than the norm... to give ourselves peace and wellbeing with our new role in life... to give ourselves a pat on the back and a huge hell yeah for our victory from yesterday as we rewind to begin another day.

My friends, cancer has the ability to reveal the very best or the very worst in us ... we are thrown into being warriors, not at our own behest but because we have no choice... great things come with great pain... great things come from people who fight...

We are but one in a group of many ... God has given us a great burden to carry but he does that for special people you know (Jesus)...much love and respect... have a great day, warriors.

> *The Lord himself goes before you and will be with you;*
> *he will never leave you nor forsake you. Do not be afraid;*
> *do not be discouraged.*
> *Deuteronomy 31:8*

Date _____

Things We Learn – Comments

Chi Ly (Head and Neck/Oral Cancer Chat and Support)
Thank you as always for your words. They are powerful.

Len Eggers (Survivors of Head and Neck Cancer)
Thank you for those inspiring words.

Randall Alderman (Cancer Survivors Network/Head and Neck)
Thank you.

Barbara Zaborski (Head and Neck/Oral Cancer Chat and Support)
You should write a book with all of your encouraging words.

Morning Thoughts:

Day's Agenda/Activities/Medications:

Dr. Appointments/Treatments/Therapies:

Bedtime Thoughts:

Date _____

Proud

Good Morning, Fighters

As I look into the mirror this morning I begin to think how many other warriors are thinking the same thoughts...

How courageous and strong are we... how mentally and emotionally tough we have to be... we must not only fight cancer, we must fight the disfigurement of our appearance... our ability to communicate... how we fight for one bite of food... how others stare at our scars, our wigs, and our bandanas as we try to cover what cancer has done... to stare at the visible scars that define us to those who don't know or understand...

We must not only fight for our very lives but we fight our butts off to have a normal life as we wear our cancer for all to see... we must not let cancer define who we are... we must wear our cancer proudly with our heads held high... we must have the confidence in ourselves to stare back at those who stare at our scars... wigs... bandanas or our disfigurement and give them the biggest smile that says... "Yes I have cancer and I fight my butt off I am a proud fighter and survivor"... make them understand that what they are staring at is more strength than they could imagine...

To every single one of you who are in the fight, I am proud to call you brother... sister... or friend. we have a common goal and that is to win... to beat cancer... I know how tough and resilient we have to be to fight like we do... we fight together... we win the battle together... we win this war together ...

> *The Lord is my rock, my fortress, and my savior;*
> *my God is my rock, in whom I find protection.*
> *He is my shield. The power that saves me and*
> *my place of safety.*
> *Psalm 18:2*

Date _____
Proud – Comments

Shannon Valasek (Cancer Support Group for Patients and Their Families)
Love this. I may steal this.

Zuri Chavez Alonzo (Survivors of Head and Neck Cancer)
Thanks for sharing. It keeps our head held high.

Dorie Erma Westring (Cancer Support Group)
Thank you for all of us. Know you are loved in this group.

Morning Thoughts:

Day's Agenda/Activities/Medications:

Dr. Appointments/Treatments/Therapies:

Bedtime Thoughts:

Date _____
Caregiver

Good Morning, Fighters

As we awake this morning I am thinking about cancer and how it affects our lives and who we are... how it affects our personal and professional lives as well as our relationships with friends... family and loved ones...

This thought process made me think about taking the focus off of us and our fight and putting it on those that care for us... "our caregivers."

My caregiver is my wife... for over half our marriage of 15 years... she has been my caregiver... my companion... my love... she has been by my side through it all... I can't imagine what our caregivers go through watching us in pain from fighting... bleeding from surgery ... burned from radiation and sick from chemo... they have to watch us struggle to get out of bed... help us find the strength to meet each day ... they comfort us and make life worth living...

Your caregiver could be a spouse or partner... a child... a friend or sibling... a doctor or nurse... therapist or social worker... whoever they are they are the most amazing people on earth... as the saying goes (caregivers have a special place in heaven)... our caregivers put our lives ahead of their own... they clean... feed... chauffer and nurture us... they are very special human beings...

Let's make today our caregiver's day ... let's show them the love and gratitude that they deserve... give them the biggest hug and kiss... tell them thank you... take them to lunch or a movie or do something that makes them happy ... put them first today ...

To my wife and caregiver... thank you for what you do and have done for me throughout this very difficult and trying time... I love and respect you as not only my wife but as a person as well... I thank you for everything...(today do this for your caregiver... you won't regret it)...

As soon as I pray, you answer me; you encourage me by giving
me strength.
Psalm 138:3

Date _____

Caregiver – Comments

Ana Maria Escalona (Survivors of Tongue Cancer)
I have missed your wonderful and inspirational messages. You make me productive and happy...

Edna Mitchell Montez (Cancer Support Group)
Hats off to you. You are our rock.

Mike Minton (Head and Neck/Oral Cancer Chat and Support)
Very true. Thank you for making me remember that.

Morning Thoughts:

Day's Agenda/Activities/Medications:

Dr. Appointments/Treatments/Therapies:

Bedtime Thoughts:

Date _____
Rhyme

Good Morning, Fighters

As doubt fills our brains...
as the poison fills our veins...
the radiation is insane...
all the surgical scars remain...
our bodies are in pain...
trying to eat is in vain...
weight we try to gain...
our hair falls out like rain...
on our thoughts we place the blame...
fighting cancer is no game...
cancer, I will hold you at bay...
and scream not today...
simply go away ...
you will not ruin my day...
against you I will pray...
to my life you have no say...
so get the hell out of my way...
I will fight you come what may...
in the end I will be ok...
if we live a life of inspiration...
if our attitude is one of motivation...
our fight is once in a generation ...
then our recovery will be an absolute sensation...

> *But each day the Lord pours his unfailing love upon me.*
> *And though each night I sing his songs, praying to God*
> *who gives me life.*
> *Psalm 42:8*

Date _____
Rhyme – Comments

Sara Eroz (Survivors of Tongue Cancer)
Yes... absolutely... fine writing.

Jessie Zimmer (Cancer Survivors Network - Head and Neck)
I want to tell you since I've been reading your blogs—they continue to give me reason to live... thank you and God bless you.

Linda Nordell (Head and Neck/Oral Cancer Chat and Support)
Awesome my friend!!

Morning Thoughts:

Day's Agenda/Activities/Medications

Dr. Appointments/Treatments/Therapies:

Bedtime Thoughts:

Date _____
Remission

Good Morning, Fighters

The power in the simple phrase... "You are in remission"... four words we all want to hear... need to hear... ..pray to hear... we fight every second of every minute of every hour of every day to tell friends... family and loved ones, "I am in remission"... to hear those beautiful words and celebrate life again...

Before cancer... before this disease changed my life... before all of the tough decisions ... and the life choices that cancer brings... before this disease had such a profound impact on friends, family and my significant other... I would hear this phrase... but it had no meaning to me at the time... it was a ubiquitous phrase... it was a few words thrown together... it had no substance... it was a phrase that before cancer I really did not understand its true meaning and the power it held...

After being in the fight against cancer... this phrase now carries the weight of the world... it is a phrase that every person in this fight and those that care for them pray for... hope for...to put their very existence on... being able to say those 4 beautiful words: "I am in remission" ... how our journey can be summed up in 4 words... how 4 words can define us... can define our fight... can freeze us at a place in time... we fight our butts off to hear those final 4 words... "You are in remission"... a more beautiful phrase I have never heard...

> *When doubts filled my mind your comfort*
> *gave me renewed hope and cheer.*
> *Psalm 94:19*

Date _____
Remission – Comments

Heather Konombo (Survivors of Tongue Cancer)
Thank you for those words. God is good... so good...

Valerie L. Gregory (Cancer Support Group)
Amen. Wonderful, as always.

Alexzandra Harris (Cancer Support Group)
This is beautiful...

Morning Thoughts:

Day's Agenda/Activities/Medications:

Dr. Appointments/Treatments/Therapies:

Bedtime Thoughts:

Date _____
Day of Rest

Good Morning, Fighters

As I awake this fine morning I began thinking, enough with the struggling... the fighting... the pushing... it all takes such a toll on us physically... mentally and emotionally... today let's just be... take a deep breath and just exist... clear our minds and nourish our souls... we not only fight physical pain... we fight to walk... to eat... to speak... to clean ourselves ... to get dressed... take our meds... to work... to give attention to our kids and grandkids... at times we may even fight to breathe... our emotions are on high alert at all times because of the physicality of this disease and the stress it puts on our bodies...(we need rest).

Today let's relax and watch a movie... go to church... have lunch with family and friends...sit in the park and let the day consume you... read a favorite book...or go to a movie you have been meaning to see for a while... call that person in your life who motivates you...talk to someone who makes you smile... do whatever it is that makes you happy...

My friends, we deserve happiness... we deserve to laugh...we deserve to enjoy the life that we fight so hard for... the life that surrounds us... we deserve to have rest and relaxation...we deserve life... we fight too hard not to live... strength needs rest...courage needs rest... resilience needs rest... we, my friends, need rest... so let's let our bodies rest...let our minds rest... we can only fight so hard for so long... let's catch our breath and just be. enjoy today for all it brings. for tomorrow we fight again...

He lets me rest in green pastures and meadows,
he leads me beside peaceful streams, God lets
me rest my soul. The peace you bring as I turn
my heart towards you.
Psalm 23:2

Date _____

Strongest

Good Morning, Fighters

The strongest people are not those that show off or flaunt their strength... or flex their muscles for all to see... that run marathons or fight in cages or rings... that use their strength for money or fame... true strength is not measured by a few minutes in the ring or a few hours on the field...

True strength belongs to those who fight battles others know nothing about... true strength cannot be measured by simply winning or losing but is measured by survival... true strength is someone who fights every minute of every hour of every day... that fights battles others cannot comprehend ... true strength is someone who gets out of bed every day and fights until exhaustion ... true strength fights an opponent with limitless energy that wants nothing more than to expose our weakness and break our spirit to literally try and steal our lives... an opponent that isn't there for a few minutes or a few hours... true strength fights 24/7/365... true strength fights for survival...fights for a normal life... fights for friends and family... for children and grandchildren ... true strength fights for love of life... fights so others can gain from that pain... fights to inspire... to watch the sun come up... to say good morning to loved ones... true strength fights for another day... another month... another year...

We are true strength... we are some of the strongest people on earth... not because we choose to be but because we have to be... we must fight for our very lives and the people that love us...

The earnest prayer of a righteous person has
great power and produces wonderful results.
James 5:6

Date _____
Strongest – Comments

Derek Morgan (Cancer Support Group)
God you nailed it brother...you brought tears to my eyes.

Prophetess BJ Hodge (Cancer Support Group for Patients and Their Families)
You say exactly how I feel. God is good.

Suzie Ehrlich Seed (Head and Neck/Oral Cancer Chat and Support)
Love this post and I really needed to hear this right now. Thank you.

Morning Thoughts:

Day's Agenda/Activities/Medications:

Dr. Appointments/Treatments/Therapies:

Bedtime Thoughts:

Date _____
Beautiful Day

Good Morning, Fighters

Yesterday was one of the greatest days of my life... it was a day that makes fighting this disease worth every second... we found out that my beautiful baby girl is having a beautiful baby girl of her own... God has truly blessed us...

I have learned while fighting this disease that my life has opened up... I am able to see life more clearly...I am able to see the good in people and in relationships... my friends, there is life after cancer... I view life in a whole new way... with a new approach to a new beginning... I embrace life and what it offers much more now than before... it seems as if I have lived two separate lives... before cancer I would put myself first... my life was more about me and not about us... but after fighting cancer I now understand that putting others first is essential to a successful and rewarding existence... I have learned that I am small but not insignificant in this world... I've learned that family and friends are precious ... that relationships need to be cultivated and watered every day with understanding and love...my life is now less about me and more about we... I've learned if you put others first you will never be last... I am now more at peace with myself than ever before...

My friends, cancer can actually make you a better person, a better you...I now count my blessings, not my money... I now count my relationships, not my things... I now count on others, not just myself... cancer can make you or break you... cancer can turn you into a bigger person and a better person... the choice is ultimately up to you, my friends...

> *God's way is perfect. All the Lord's promises*
> *prove true. He is a shield for all who look to*
> *him for protection.*
> *2 Samuel 22:31*

He is risen... Christ, our Lord.

Date _____
Beautiful Day – Comments

Patty Joiner (Survivors of Tongue Cancer)
Thank you for your words of wisdom and inspiration.

Juliette Marie (Survivors of Tongue Cancer)
You are an inspiration and a warrior.

Kenny Fields (Head and Neck/Oral Cancer Chat and Support)
Thank you for your powerful messages!!

Morning Thoughts:

Day's Agenda/Activities/Medications:

Dr. Appointments/Treatments/Therapies:

Bedtime Thoughts:

Date _____

Painful

Good Morning, Fighters

Pain, the worst of the four-letter words... and there are some bad ones out there... lol... so many of us are not just fighting cancer... we are also fighting the pain... not only physically but mentally and emotionally as well... it is a pain we would not wish on our worst enemy ... it is a pain we thought we would never feel... a pain we thought we would never face... it's a pain that makes us think twice before we get out of bed... a pain at times that makes us question the fight... it frustrates the hell out of us... it makes us question if what we are doing is ever enough... it tests us as warriors... it tests us as fighters... the surgeries are painful...the radiation is painful...the chemo makes us sick and angry... sometimes it feels like we are all alone in this world of pain... isolated and alone in our existence...

Every surgery ... every radiation treatment... every time we sit and allow poison to drip into our veins... we think of the pain... we get angry at the pain... we have unbridled hate at the pain... we curse and throw things because of the pain... this disease wants us to see life through the lens of loss... pain... darkness... sickness and loneliness...but there is a different lens if we choose to use it... one of compassion... hope... strength... courage... patience and resiliency...

Are we going to have bad days... absolutely we are...are we going to have days when we want to hide under the covers... absolutely we are... when we fight as hard as we do...we sometimes forget that there is another side to our fight... we are also going to have good days...days when we get up and feel better than expected... some days we may wake up in a great mood for no real reason...we will have days when we see real progress in our journey ... days of being able to eat again... talk again...walk again... sleep again... where the healing is just around the corner. To look in the mirror and be able to see ourselves again... to see an even better person in our reflection...

For I do everything through Christ who gives me strength
he gives me strength when things get tough. I know all
will be well because you are with me.
Philippians 4:13

Date _____

Painful – Comments

Tina Habegger Trepenowski (Cancer Support Group)
This is so true... thank you for making me understood.

Julie Marie Paolella Jardonek (Cancer Support Group)
I read those beautiful words. Thank you warrior.

Cheryl Delapp Rice (Head and Neck/Oral Cancer Chat and Support)
You are a huge part of my journey! Even on bad days we are healing. Thank you.

Morning Thoughts:

Day's Agenda/Activities/Medications:

Dr. Appointments/Treatments/Therapies:

Bedtime Thoughts:

Date _____

The Long Road

Good Morning, Fighters

A quick trip down memory lane: surgery

I'm a fighter but to be honest I was scared... the 15-hour surgery scared me to death (no pun intended)... as I slowly opened my eyes after surgery ... the first thing I remember was the look of horror, pity, and love on my family's faces... I could see the tears on my wife's, my daughter's, and my mom's cheeks as my son, my dad, and my best friend held back their tears because that is what men are supposed to do... dried blood was on my neck and chest... and thru the haze of my drug-addled mind I had one lucid thought... "the fight has just begun"... and through the morphine... hydrocodone and Ativan I could still feel the physical pain I had never felt before... the physical pain was but a small part of my fear... mentally I was running in circles because of the unknown... thinking what is next... as I laid in bed in the ICU I felt loneliness after my family and friends paid their respects and left... I understood they had a life to live... errands to run... business to attend to... I laid there alone feeling the complete weight of my situation and slowly understanding and coming to grips with my "new normal"... my "new life"... my "new reality"...

Radiation:

My next memory was being held down to a table by a mask that felt like the Spanish inquisition or something out of a Michael Myers or Jason Voorhees movie. I was petrified thinking this whole situation couldn't be real... while a huge machine whirs around my head... burning away the cancer but also burning my skin... my hair... my life... I felt like my face and my psyche were on fire... thinking the whole time, "Is this real?"...

Chemo:

Having the patience to sit for hours while poison is being forced into my veins to kill the cancer... but I could also feel the drugs killing me from the inside out... healing me but killing me at the same time... making me sick... making me fearful... making me question... making me accept a different life...

My friends, this whole process can bring the strongest of warriors to their knees... it can have us questioning ourselves on so many different fronts...

I must admit, I cried like an infant when no one was around... I felt sorry for myself... I was the main act at my pity party... it's okay to feel this way... we have all been through a lot... we've been through what others can't imagine... we feel the physical pain that makes us want to scream... to try and understand the mental pain of the unknown and why me? Along with the exhaustion of trying to control the emotional pain of the disease... this journey is not for the faint of heart...it is for the strongest of us to traverse... I truly believe that God gives the heaviest burden to the strongest people... imagine the burden he gave his son... Jesus not only carried the physical burden of the cross... he carried the heaviest burden of all our souls...

Believe in yourself and who you are... and you will beat this disease... 'you better believe it'... (pun intended)...

> *Then your light will break forth like the dawn; and your healing will quickly appear and your righteousness will go before you. The glory of God will be in your rear guard and when you call out, the Lord will answer you: you will cry for help and God will say, "Here I am, my child." Isaiah 58:8-9*

Date _____

The Long Road – Comments

Elizabeth F. Walker (Survivors of Tongue Cancer)
Thank you for teaching us to be strong so we can teach strength and love.

Michael Stevenson (Cancer Support Group)
You are an inspiration to us all every day. If it weren't for your positive words, I would be in trouble...

Nathalie Dimech (Head and Neck/Oral Cancer Chat and Support)
Your words always encourage me to move on since every word is true.

Morning Thoughts:

Day's Agenda/Activities/Medications:

Dr. Appointments/Treatments/Therapies:

Bedtime Thoughts:

Date _____

Endurance

Good Morning, Fighters

As we open our eyes and reality sets in... we shake out the cobwebs as our hope fades into our pain from the night before... hoping this was nothing but a bad dream... we think how this nasty opponent tries to control every facet of who we are... not only are we in the fight for our very lives... we also have bills to pay... relationships to manage... households to run... cleaning to do... errands to take care of... life to live...we manage all of this as we fight incredible pain... at the same time we struggle to eat... to talk... to even breathe... we must control our emotions because we want to scream... as the frustration consumes us we push through... we have a life to live... and others who count on us... we endure all of life's challenges while fighting this unrelenting opponent... we manage life through pain... my friends, that is a hero... not catching a touchdown pass or hitting a home run... kicking a goal or sinking a 3-pointer at the buzzer...

A true hero:

goes through radiation and still vacuums...

goes through chemo and still cooks dinner...

goes through reconstructive surgery and makes a living...

is told that cancer has won yet continues to fight their butts off anyway...

is close to death and still gives every ounce of energy to those they love...

that, my friends, is a hero...

that, my friends, describes us...

that, my friends, is who we are...

never forget your strength... your courage...

never forget your heart and soul...

because you, my friends, we are the very definition of a hero...

> *When troubles of any kind come your way consider it an*
> *opportunity for great joy. For you know that when your*
> *faith is tested, your endurance has a chance to grow.*
> *James 1:2-3*

Date _____
Endurance – Comments

Tammi Yoder Wengerd (Cancer Support Group)
Thank you. Your inspiration has gotten me up an out of bed for the first time in a week. I think I will try weeding my garden. Thank you.

Marilyn Ruedisveli (Head and Neck/Oral Cancer Chat and Support)
You have me proclaiming I'm a hero today. Thank you for the reminder.

Michelle Kolessar (Head and Neck/Oral Cancer Chat and Support)
So well written. You are a diamond.

Morning Thoughts:

Day's Agenda/Activities/Medications:

Dr. Appointments/Treatments/Therapies:

Bedtime Thoughts:

Date _____
10 Minutes

Good Morning, Fighters

Cancer forces us to make more decisions in the first 10 minutes of our morning than most people make all day... we feel more emotions in the first 10 minutes of our morning than most people will feel in a week... we see more scars in the mirror than most people will see in their entire lifetime...

We stare at ourselves in the mirror trying to remember what we looked like before all of this... we gaze upon a new reality... a new life... a new hope... the mirror is brutally honest... it does not lie... our reflection can show us a different person or it can show us the same person, just different circumstances ... in our reflection we can see strength... courage... resiliency and character... we see the bravest person we have the privilege to know... we see how we look but it does not determine who we are... we see someone who fights their butt off day after day to lead a normal and rewarding life... we see someone who fights battles others can't imagine... we see a father or mother... a grandad or grandma... we see a brother or sister... a son or daughter...

We can't forget who we were before all of this... before this disease so unceremoniously entered our lives because that person still exists... others count on that person to be there...In that reflection we see a fighter... we see a survivor... we see a winner...

"In this reflection we see us."

> *Give, and you will receive. Your gift will return to you*
> *in full—pressed down, shaken together to make room*
> *for more, running over, and poured into your lap.*
> *Luke 6:30*

Date _____

10 Minutes – Comments

Debbie Dicker Ruscetti (Survivors of Tongue Cancer)
My favorite winner. Everything you write is a winner.

Catherine L. Anderson (Head and Neck/Oral Cancer Chat and Support)
I needed to hear this and yesterday's message from you that when you get knocked down you get right back up.

Liz St. Pierre (Head and Neck/Oral Cancer Chat and Support)
Thank you I needed to hear this today. I needed to read this today.

Morning Thoughts:

Day's Agenda/Activities/Medications:

Dr. Appointments/Treatments/Therapies:

Bedtime Thoughts:

Date _____

Definition

Good Morning, Fighters

Webster's definition of strength:

capacity for exertion or endurance in a physical...intellectual or emotional way:force... vigor... power... solidity... toughness...

What was our definition of strength before cancer infiltrated our lives... what is our definition now... how did we describe the word strength before our fight began... what is our new description after going through the pain and frustrations this disease puts upon us with all the life-altering treatments... has the definition changed... has it changed in our minds and in our hearts and souls as well...

This one word that now describes us in its entirety ... this one word that is now interwoven into who we are as a fighter and a warrior... this one word whose meaning now describes us perfectly... (strength... exertion... endurance... force... vigor... power... solidity and toughness) ... this word that now encapsulates our journey... a global definition of us... we have no idea how strong we really are until now... we exceed all boundaries that the word strength entails... we now rise above and transcend the very definition of strength...

We are amazing human beings with a spirit few will ever know... we have a special strength others can't imagine...when we look into the mirror this fine morning we see a true fighter... a true warrior... a true winner looking back at us...let's give that warrior a smile, a wink, and a nod... let's give ourselves the respect and credit we deserve... we must love ourselves and who we are... because the first thing this disease will try to take from you is you... to my brothers and sisters in the fight... it gives me great solace to know that you are out there... to know that there are others who think about and can empathize with our unique situation... to know we are loved... that we are understood and respected... to simply know we are not alone...

I pray that God, the source of hope, will fill you
completely with joy, love and peace because you

trust in him. And you can always count on him.
Romans 15:13

Date _____
Definition – Comments

Carla Van Vranken (Survivors of Tongue Cancer)
You are unstoppable. You are awesome.

Rebecca Corbitt (Head and Neck/Oral Cancer Chat and Support)
Joined this group 2 years ago. Didn't realize how much I need you. Thank you. You've saved me.

Jessie Zemmer (Cancer Survivors Network - Head and Neck)
Just knowing you are there is comforting. Thank you.

Morning Thoughts:

Day's Agenda/Activities/Medications:

Dr. Appointments/Treatments/Therapies:

Bedtime Thoughts:

Date _____

Under My Breath

Good Morning, Fighters

Cancer, you have worn me out... forced me to my knees... made me ask God 'why me' a hundred times... you have made me question myself... you pushed me to tears of anger and frustration... you brought me to the very threshold of hate and fear... I know there is still good in this world no matter how you try to cover my eyes... I know there are great days ahead even though you try to darken my heart... I can see the blessings you try to hide from me... cancer, my eyes are open to your unfairness... my heart is untethered to your hate... you are a formidable opponent but my faith is stronger ... the fight is worth it...

Yesterday I experienced a beautiful sunrise and an even more spectacular sunset... with a great day in between... yesterday was one of those days we fight for... that give us a reason to live and love... a reason to hope...

Just a short time ago I began the fight of a lifetime... my doctor had given me the grim diagnosis of stage 4 scc (squamous cell carcinoma) of the tongue and lymph nodes... my future was uncertain at best... I had a 50/50 shot at beating this disease... but 9 surgeries... 35 rounds of radiation and hours of poison being forced into my veins I beat this disease... I beat cancer ... I fought with every fiber of my being... I fought for days like yesterday that make the fight worth it... I fought to live... I fought to enjoy life... I fought for family and friends... to my brothers and sisters in the fight. To those of you who are asking themselves is this all worth it... to those of you on the edge... the fight is worth it, I promise you... my friends, we fight with everything we are... we fight mind... body and soul...knowing that we will have those perfect days that make this fight worth it...

> *Blessed is the one who perseveres under trial because,*
> *having stood the test, that person will receive the crown*
> *of life that the Lord has promised to those who love him.*
> *James 1:12*

Date _____

Under My Breath – Comments

BK Crume McAnn (Cancer Support Group)
You are an inspiration to so many lives.

Peter Schules (Cancer Support Group)
A very eloquent expression of the emotions that we feel when we experience cancer.

Patricia Cypoutisto (Cancer Support Group for Patients and Their Families)
This is how I feel when I read your posts; it's like you are talking to me when I read… thank you so much!

Morning Thoughts:

Day's Agenda/Activities/Medications:

Dr. Appointments/Treatments/Therapies:

Bedtime Thoughts:

Date _____

A Perfect Dream

Good Morning, Fighters

Yesterday was a day I thought I would never see... a day that I could only wake up from as it faded into the past... a day I tried to grab like a whisp of smoke... a day that I shed many a tear thinking about the beauty of what that day would hold... a day made up of many perfect dreams that slipped through my fingers because of a disease that ravaged my mind... body and soul... a disease that made me question my self-worth with each passing pain-filled day... a day that I believed was out of my reach... I was a breath away from giving in to this disease... it was just too painful physically ... mentally and emotionally... it had beaten me down... I was exhausted from the onslaught of the negative effects of cancer...

One day when I was at the end of my rope I dug through my wallet and took out the pictures of the 3 reasons I wanted to live... the 3 reasons to fight this hell on earth... I gazed for what seemed like hours at my children's pictures... and made a decision to fight with every fiber of who I am... to weave myself back into the fabric of life... I am now being blessed for that decision... that decision has given me a chance to hold a perfectly beautiful little human baby that has my blood flowing through his veins... I am now engaged in a life with hope... love and happiness ... I can now hold a grandson and will have another new addition... a baby girl in October to hold just like ledger... I can now hold and love a beautiful wife... 3 children and 4 grandchildren ... all loves of my life... and I can continue to fight mind... body and soul to watch each of them prosper and make their mark on this big world of ours... yes, I was at a crossroad in my life when I could have chosen to give up or fight... I chose to fight and am now being unbelievably blessed for that choice... has it been easy... hell no... has it been worth it ... hell yeah...

My brothers and sisters, much love and respect... continue to fight because I'm telling you right now the fight is worth it...

> *So let us come boldly to the throne of our gracious God.*
> *There we will receive his mercy and we will find grace to*

help us when we need it the most.
Hebrews 4:16

Date _____
A Perfect Dream - Comments

Cara Lenbo (Cancer Support Group)
Today has been rough. My complications are so serious and I needed to hear your encouraging words. Thank you and God bless you.

Jackie Croft (Facebook, my timeline, July 31, 2021)
My goodness, tears fell from my eyes. You are amazing and with so many words. I love you my friend; you are a strong human being. God is on your side.

Dana Harrison (Facebook, my timeline, July 31, 2021)
Beautiful... well said... the love makes it all worthwhile. To fight is all I have. I will never be a victim again. I won't let it have that control over my soul, thanks to you.

Morning Thoughts:

Day's Agenda/Activities/Medications:

Dr. Appointments/Treatments/Therapies:

Bedtime Thoughts:

Date _____

A Special Day #1

Good Morning, Fighters

Today is a very special day... today is a day I thought I would never see... a day I could only dream about... a day when I began this fight... I had a 30% chance that I would see a day like today ... what is special about today, you ask... ..what is not special about today, I say... there doesn't have to be a special occasion to make today the greatest day in our lives... how about we opened our eyes to a brand-new day... we can hear the birds chirping outside... the small sounds the wind creates... to hug a child or grandchild ... to smile at a stranger... to watch the day unfold... the chance to take in the beauty of a loved one... to be able to impact the world in our own way... this day is why we push through the pain and frustrations ... this day is a moment in life we cherish even more because of the fight we endure... every morning should be unbelievably special... every day a blessing... I know sometimes it doesn't seem worth it but that's when we must fight twice as hard to reach for tomorrow and you will get to days like today...

We had no idea how strong we are until now... how we exceed all boundaries that strength entails... how we rise above and transcend the very definition of strength... how when we are at our weakest and most vulnerable, we still have more strength than can be imagined ... my friends, we have crushed 15-hour surgeries ... we are fighting or have fought through being burned relentlessly by radiation... we have sat for hours while poison is forced through our veins... we have endured all of these life-altering treatments... we have fought through pain that can bring the toughest to their knees... after going through all we have how could every day not be special... how could every day not be the best day ever... how could we not wake up with "Thank you, God" on our minds... what we go through in one day most people do not go through in their entire lifetime... we should embrace every day of life with a smile on our face and a song in our heart and enjoy this life we have been given... there doesn't have to be a special occasion to make today special... just being able to see all of the blessings of today should make this day a very special day...

Jesus said, "In the time of my favor I heard you and in the days of salvation I helped you." I tell you now is the day and time of God's favor.
2 Corinthians 6:2

Date _____
Special Day – Comments

Kirsty Ellen-Green (Survivors of Tongue Cancer)
Such wonderful words. I am finding this very hard but your words make me feel better.

Donna L. Martin Gates (Head and Neck/Oral Cancer Chat and Support)
I am happy to stand with you warrior. You are a true inspiration to me.

Judie Smith (Head and Neck/Oral Cancer Chat and Support)
I look forward to reading your posts every morning. They are the highlight of my day! Your optimism and positive attitude make me strive to be a better person.

Morning Thoughts:

Day's Agenda/Activities/Medications:

Dr. Appointments/Treatments/Therapies:

Bedtime Thoughts:

Date _____
A Special Day #2

Good Morning, Fighters

Today is another very special day ... today is a day I thought I would never see... today I am in remission from stage 4 oral cancer... 11 surgeries... 35 rounds of radiation... chemo and 4 hospital stays... after all of that I can honestly say I beat you, cancer... I kept punching... I kept kicking... I kept fighting until you couldn't take it anymore and said, "This fighter is just too much... I'm outta here"... and good riddance to you, cancer... I was diagnosed in 2013 and fought for years to get to where I am today ... the fight of a lifetime... the fight of my life... yes, cancer, you left your mark on me physically... but you couldn't take me down... mentally I beat you... mentally I won... yes, there are a few after-effects because of the treatments... but I beat you... I sent you packing... you ran away from me with your tail between your legs... I kicked your butt... yes, my friends, no matter what stage you're in... even stage 4 ... you can win... you can beat this disease... whatever cancer can throw at you... you can fight back and make up your mind that you will survive... that you can win... we are amazing human beings with a spirit few will ever know... today is a day of positivity... optimism... peace... perseverance and potential... we are all brothers and sisters in this fight... no matter where you are in your fight... you know that you can beat cancer... you can win... just keep fighting and never... never... never give up...

Thank you for reading my book of inspiration and perspiration ... lol... it was definitely a labor of love...I hope that by reading this I have helped you in some small way to beat cancer... to beat this disease... providing moral support... motivation and inspiration are key components to beating this disease... there is only so much your medical team can do for you physically ... after that... beating cancer is physically... mentally and emotionally... ultimately up to you...

> *Trust in the Lord with all your heart and lean not on your own understanding: In all your ways submit to Him and He will make your path straight.*
> *I choose this hour to trust in You, our Lord.*
> *Proverbs 3:5-6*

Date _____

A Special Day – Comments

Ron Sparkman (Cancer Support Group for Patients and Their Families)
I needed this today. Thank you.

William Meyers (Cancer Support Group for Patients and Their Families)
This inspires me and gives me hope.

Thomas Naveaux (Survivors of Head and Neck Cancer)
Your daily posts are a true inspiration to me and they are the first thing I read each morning.

Gail Gluck Levinton (Survivors of Head and Neck Cancer)
Wow. Great job. I needed this inspiration today.

Donna Craft (Survivors of Head and Neck Cancer)
Thank you for the positive thoughts every day.

Patricia Hartwell (Cancer Support Group)
You are amazing... You give me a great positive attitude.

Nick Potohney (Cancer Support Group)
Way to kick ass. Please keep inspiring us.

Lea Preciado (Cancer Support Group)
You give us hope.

Annie Harrison (Cancer Support Group)
Well done. I'm at a loss for words. Well done.

Erin Farrell Parker (Survivors of Tongue Cancer)
What an awesome piece to read.

Brenda Sue Henthorne Morris (Survivors of Tongue Cancer)

Wonderful, just wonderful.

Amy Elizabeth (Survivors of Tongue Cancer)
You are amazing.

Jimmy Cook (Head and Neck/Oral Cancer Chat and Support)
Awesome. Thank you for giving us hope and daily inspiration needed.

Josie O'Shea (Head and Neck/Oral Cancer Chat and Support)
Love to read your daily posts. You have helped me so much. This post is now my favorite.

Jodie Smith (Head and Neck/Oral Cancer Chat and Support)
As always thank you for your encouragement and positivity. You are the most incredible and inspirational person I have ever encountered

Morning Thoughts:

Day's Agenda/Activities/Medications:

Dr. Appointments/Treatments/Therapies:

Bedtime Thoughts:

CPSIA information can be obtained
at www.ICGtesting.com
Printed in the USA
LVHW021811080323
741205LV00003B/430